WRECK AND REC

WRECK AND RECOVERY

Vehicles • Emergency Equipment • Rescue Techniques

ALAN THOMAS

Patrick Stephens
Wellingborough, Northamptonshire

First published in 1987

British Library Cataloguing in Publication Data

Thomas, Alan, *1936–*
Wreck and recovery
1. Vehicle wrecking services—Great Britain
I. Title
388.3′2   TA1145

ISBN 0-85059-857-5

Cover illustration: *Leyland Roadtrain 6 by 2 with
a lifting centre axle, owned by Arlington Motors
(Willesden). Wreckers International fitted the chassis
with modified Holmes 750 twin boom
recovery equipment.*

*Patrick Stephens Limited is part of the
Thorsons Publishing Group*

Printed and bound in Great Britain

Contents

Introduction

The introductions to most books end by acknowledging those who have helped in preparing them. Since *Wreck and Recovery* would otherwise have remained a stillborn idea, this book begins with warmest thanks to everyone who by their help and friendship made it possible for me to write it.

I must extend my gratitude further to the good friends who have provided many of the pictures, particularly Tom Carruthers, Peter Cosby, David Doe, Reg Forester-Smith, James Foster, Ron Grice, John Hancock, Gavin Kane, Andy Lambert, Philip Lund, Doug Maltby, Tim Nicholson, Jonathan Pye, Phil Renno, Sergeant T. G. Sheppard and Paul Stember. Without leave to rifle the cupboards, drawers and old envelopes that comprise their various filing systems this would have been a bare work indeed. Gentlemen: thank you. And to any I have disgracefully forgotten to mention by name my apologies, but still sincere thanks.

Pleasant duty done, now to the reason for writing the book. Although vehicle recovery is as old as the transport industry it is only in recent years that conditions have created a need for professional recovery operators capable of using to full effect a wide range of very specialized equipment. *Wreck and Recovery* is intended to be an exploration of this still-new aspect of road transport — and a recognition of the debt owed by every road user to the recovery men, unsung heroes who cope with horrific events as part of their daily round, and who the rest of us should honour alongside the police and fire services.

Alan Thomas, AIRTE
London SE3, February 1987

Chapter 1

A fast-changing business

Vehicle recovery is a curiously secret business. Although it is an essential part of the road transport industry most drivers, happily, have almost no contact with it. When they do meet a recovery job in progress it probably means no more to them than a traffic hold-up, or a fleeting glimpse of something happening on the other carriageway.

In large part, no doubt, this lack of awareness is a result of recovery almost always being bad news for someone; nobody wants to spend much time thinking about the nastier things that can happen to them on the road. In addition, recovery has traditionally been only a part, usually a small and obscure part, of a garage or some other business. But times are changing; not only is recovery rapidly becoming a high investment industry in its own right, but modern operating conditions are forcing road users to rely on professional recovery teams on the sorts of occasions when, not so long ago, they would probably have managed quite well without having to call for help.

These changing conditions are also having a big effect on the ways in which this rapidly emerging industry is organized, and in the kinds of equipment that it uses. Again, not so long ago, a couple of army surplus trucks with hand-operated cranes on their backs would be the cream of any fleet and well able to cope with most 'heavy' jobs, whilst a big old limousine chassis, with the back of the body sawn off and an angle-iron jib added, easily handled any car that came to grief. That sort of equipment was worth hardly anything and could be left against the yard wall for weeks if necessary, turning out only rarely and when it did crewed by anyone who could be spared, and the apprentice. Now, not only have commercial vehicle weights very nearly doubled, but every kind of modern vehicle large or small is designed in such a way that its structure cannot take any lift or pull it was not designed to take. In addition to this fragility, the value of all vehicles has gone up enormously and it is all too easy for a careless recovery team, or a badly equipped one, to cause irreparable damage to a vehicle.

If modern casualties are valuable, needing appropriate equipment to recover them without unnecessary further damage, then modern recovery trucks also have become very specialized — which means they cost a great deal of money. Inevitably such investment for occasional use soon becomes too high for an ordinary garage to face, and so there is a growing number of firms who do nothing but recovery work. Because they specialize, they can keep their equipment busy and justify the expense of training and employing skilful operators.

The very nature of road accidents has changed out of all recognition. Not so long ago collision speeds were low; now they are high. Then roads were narrow and badly lit; now they are fast and well illuminated. Then railways carried the bulk of passenger and goods traffic; now road transport is the lifeblood of industry. Then traffic stayed at home in bad weather; now, in fog or ice, the cars, the coaches and the lorries keep rolling. As a result of huge improvements in road and vehicle building, in technology and in driver training there are far fewer accidents now than there used to be, but those that do happen tend to be more serious and multi-vehicle pile-ups have become almost the hallmark of present-day 'incidents'.

The combination of high speeds and modern roads has added greatly to the damage a casualty vehicle can suffer. Lofty embankments, viaducts, deep cuttings, wide-sweeping elevated junctions — all virtually unknown on British roads until recent times — create taxing problems. Every recovery operator has stories of cars found deep in woods below road level, whose path is signposted by broken branches — ten feet above the ground; of apparently sturdy trees that have all too clearly bent before some careering vehicle — and straightened again afterwards; of heavy lorries that have vaulted from elevated roadways to land in a river or soft marsh below; of cars that somehow bury themselves deep in pedestrian subways; of vehicles of all kinds that end up straddling waterways.

There are problems of another kind too, for now that road transport carries almost all freight some of the substances that are hauled can be terrifying once their containers begin to leak or if they are mishandled in any way. Fortunately the number of headline-catching disasters caused so far by such vehicles is few, so far, but enough oil and chemical industry tankers have leaked or exploded, loads of hanging meat and half-filled tankers have rolled over, and cargoes of timber or steel or machinery have broken loose and crushed passers-by to show what risks are created as soon as a vehicle loses its stability. Usually such vehicles were being driven carefully at reasonable speeds, which makes tragedy more poignant. On a strictly commercial level and even when no personal harm has been done, the contents of a lorry off the road may easily and often be worth more than twice the value of the vehicle itself. Again the cargoes can be surprising — 20 tons of ordinary-sounding foodstuffs may be a very valuable consignment, and one that rapidly spoils.

Happily the death and disaster sort of recovery work is only a small part of the workload. More frequent by far are call-outs to mechanical failures. Here the huge increase in the numbers of vehicles using the roads has added its own unacceptable risks to what were once perfectly safe practices. It used to be the regular thing, when a telephone call came in to say someone had broken down, to send out any truck that happened to be free, hitch on a bit of chain, and just tow home the casualty. A neighbour would happily do such a favour when his friend's car refused to start.

But now such assistance can easily become lethal. In amateur operations confusion is sure to set in at some point, and fast-moving traffic makes no allowance for error. All it needs is for a tow rope or chain to break, or a towing eye to pull out, and the scene is set for tragedy. If, as happens all too easily, the towed vehicle gets out of line with its rescuer and tries to overtake, the pair may well jackknife into trouble. At the very least, the complexities of modern transmissions make it necessary to be quite sure no damage will be done to a vehicle by towing it while its engine isn't running.

Equally, no longer is it safe, on most main roads, to attempt to carry out roadside repairs — stationary vehicles, particularly in poor visibility, all too easily become the focal point of a smash. It is better by far, whenever possible, to get even simple jobs off the road to a safe location.

Until very recently there was a distinction without difference between the terms 'recovery' and 'breakdown', but present-day operating conditions have led the recovery industry generally to agree among itself that it is sensible to use 'breakdown' in describing a vehicle which has failed through some fault that can be put right by a mechanic. A 'recovery' may conveniently be defined as a casualty vehicle which, for whatever reason, has to be towed or transported from the place where it came to an involuntary halt. In practice recovery itself subdivides into two main categories; simply towing away vehicles that have broken down, and retrieving and removing those that have crashed.

The great changes in operating conditions have forced equally great changes to be made in recovery equipment. When new models are being designed, exasperated recoverymen aver, the one certainty which is never borne in mind is that one day a vehicle will break down in service, or crash, and have to be rescued. They are designed to travel, not for towing. This was of less importance when all vehicles were mechanically simple and had sturdy chassis, and motor industry designers, well aware that it wasn't practical to assess all of the stresses their products would endure, built large factors of safety in to them. Now, however, modern computer techniques make it possible to calculate very accurately indeed just how strong each component part of a vehicle must be. One result of this is that unladen weights are reduced to a minimum, which is good, but there is no surplus strength for recovery crews to take advantage of, which is bad — or at best awkward.

This concentration on getting the maximum design value for money has resulted in chassisless cars with safety crumple zones front and back, and chassisless coaches and buses with huge overhangs at each end. Lorries, it is true, tend to have shorter overhangs and they usually have chassis (although many semi-trailer vans and tankers don't), but all the structural frames of these vehicles are carefully arranged to carry the designed loads in just the ways they are meant to be carried. Any attempt to make a straightforward lift at the front or rear bumper effectively adds extra loadings for which no allowance has been made, and will often cause immediate distortion of the whole vehicle. Even if it doesn't, then vibration during towing, or a clipped kerb, may be enough to trigger irreparable damage. On the other hand a flat tow, in which the transmission is driven by the road wheels and not by the engine, can quickly wreck a gearbox and drive-line. Unless it is possible virtually to dismantle the transmission, some sort of lift is, therefore, very desirable in recovering even straightforward mechanical breakdowns.

But of course every vehicle is designed to stand on its own wheels, and while standing on them to resist for a lifetime all of the shocks and loadings that will come its way. So designers of recovery equipment have been forced to move forward from the crane style of lifting unit and develop also means of lifting casualties at or close to their wheels or axles. This is rather more difficult than it sounds — in using a 'damage-free' under-reach device to make a lift at the wheels, that troublesome overhang on the casualty is effectively transferred from the failed vehicle to its rescuer, with the result that the weight imposed on the recovery unit rear axle can easily become excessive. Apart from this being illegal, safety considerations soon become significant.

An incidental but huge advantage of any modern lift-tow recovery unit is that, more often than not, one man can couple up the train and get it home without assistance. On a flat tow a competent second driver is needed.

For off-road recovery there is still little to beat a traditional twin-boom wrecker, for the versatility of these classic machines is limited only by the expertise of their operators. The two booms are in effect independent slewing cranes that can be joined when necessary; heavy duty winches form the heart of the machines, and with skilful rigging of their wire ropes twin-booms can recover a casualty from any imaginable, and some unimaginable, predicaments.

Often enough in a road traffic accident — an RTA — a vehicle has rolled and is lying on its side. The time-honoured way of getting it back on to its wheels is the obvious one, with slings wrapped round it, and a good long haul on a rope. Equally obviously the large size and tender construction of many modern vehicles means they are likely to suffer considerable damage in the process of uprighting. It was to combat this problem that air bags were developed. Three or four of these tough drum-shaped envelopes, inserted under even a large rolled vehicle and inflated by a small low pressure compressor, will get it back on to its feet again with the minimum of stress. Indeed, in all probability the windows of a coach, or the side panels of a big van will hardly be marked by the recovery operation, whatever other damage they may have already sustained.

Recovering large vehicles, using big and handsome wreckers, is clearly the glamorous end of the business, but reckoned in terms of the number of jobs done (and perhaps in overall profitability) car recovery far outstrips the heavies. In large part the same kinds of problems crop up here too, because economic and operating considerations mean that light recovery units are generally used for light work, so there is not much spare lifting capacity. The widespread use of fragile and very expensive car body trim details, like air dams and bumpers made in plastics, greatly increases the risk of damage during recovery and make it most advisable to lift a casualty from its wheels. And, again, apart from the need for a suitable second driver, there is always the likelihood of transmission damage in a flat tow.

Before motorways and long-distance motoring jointly became a way of life, the garage tow-truck was a useful means of generating work for its home workshop — after all, having towed in a breakdown, who else would get the repair job? Then several things happened, not least of them being the rise of the company car, belonging to a large fleet that is centrally administered. Company cars are driven by drivers in smart clothes to whom the car is a tool to be used for business and — most important — pleasure, which must be replaced quickly when it fails. At much the same time those cars became a great deal more complicated and virtually incapable of roadside repair for any but the most trivial ailments. As a result, and all too often, local garages found themselves turning into mere staging posts for breakdowns that were to be dispatched elsewhere for repair; to a contracted repair shop miles away perhaps, or to a franchised dealer fully equipped with diagnostic and other special equipment needed.

All things considered, it is not surprising that the big growth in light recovery is among transporter operators and transporters, which carry a car or light van on a suitably decked truck and with all the wheels off the road.

With a sharp eye for a growing market equipment makers have worked hard at developing the transporter. For infrequent use, or long journeys, users can buy what amounts to a low level platform lorry, with a sloping beaver tail and removable ramps. In the next stage of elaboration the platform body is arranged to tilt which, with ramps, gives a reasonably flat loading angle. At the top of the market are slideback bodies, which roll back partially off the carrying chassis and then tilt for easy loading. Winches and associated equipment are standard fittings so that one man can load even a large disabled car or panel van on to a transporter without assistance. Transporters have become quite elaborate, and since they are often called out to breakdowns which have full loads of passengers, well-appointed crew cabs are commonly fitted.

The idea of all wheels off the road recovery is obviously very attractive, and it would provide a near-perfect solution to the problems posed by large and fragile commercials. The snag is an economic one — an operator could hardly expect to get enough work to keep such a transporter busy, and he would still need to own conventional wrecker equipment in order to cope with all the many run of the mill jobs a transporter couldn't do. It is similar reasoning that militates against the use of conventional cranes for recovery work — despite their apparent suitability for some jobs, their cost wouldn't be justified by the amount of work they could do. Another factor in the transporter argument are the average distances covered in recoveries. Typically, cars that break down are a long way from home on business or holiday trips and their owners want them returned, however not often is a commercial vehicle towed more than a few miles from the place at which it fails. Still, it has to be said that the peculiar recovery needs of armies are very often met with a variety of transporters able to carry anything up to battle tank size and weight. Armed forces have usually led the way in developing advanced recovery equipment and techniques, and perhaps they will do so in this regard too.

While there is no doubt that recovery operators and their equipment must keep within the same overall legislation as all other road users, there is equally no doubt that in emergencies common sense is allowed to take precedence over legal niceties. Long may it be so — but the ambivalent role of vehicle recovery teams can easily put them into impossible positions, and it is high time concerted efforts were made to establish a firm and sensible framework within which the industry can work. The main difficulty stems from the fact that while police, fire and ambulance personnel are all part of the public services and make no charge, recovery companies are private concerns. They compete with each other for business, and in large part they are dependent on the police for approval of the way their businesses are run, and for future allocations of work.

The police have overall authority to co-ordinate effort at an incident; the ambulance teams are expert in first aid and lifesaving; firemen are unexcelled at dealing with fire risks and dangerous substances, and are trained in extricating trapped and injured people from crashed vehicles. Yet the recovery crews will have great mechanical power at their disposal, and probably know far more than anyone else on site about how to harness that power to stabilize crashed vehicles and prevent them from doing more harm. Furthermore, from experience they may well have a good idea of how to use the extensive equipment at their disposal to distort vehicles yet further to release trapped victims. Not a few lorry drivers are today walking about on their own legs, because recovery experts saw ways other than amputation to free them from wrecks.

Another key difference is that the responsibilities of recovery operators last much longer than those of the public service departments. With the injured safely in hospital, wreckage removed, and carriageways hosed down, police, fire, and ambulance personnel can depart to fill in report forms. But while they are doing so, the recovery teams will still be cautiously plodding back to base with, from the roadworthiness point of view, an unknown quantity on tow. There are no concessions available to them in such all-important matters as axle weights, and there would be no defence if, on the journey, the always onerous Construction and Use Regulations were transgressed.

Any mishaps in traffic or further damage to the casualty would certainly be their direct responsibility, and this liability extends to any contents of the crashed vehicle and the mischief they might cause. The list of hazardous cargoes is long and often surprising — not only petrol tankers, full or empty, are capable of creating havoc if leaking fumes should be ignited by a spark that might all too easily be generated by distorted metal rubbing against something. Essential stock in trade for any prudent recovery firm includes not only ample first-aid safety equipment and safety training, but all-risks insurance cover for a very large sum indeed.

Once the wrecker is home, parked up and ready for the next call, there begin the negotiations for payment. In most recovery jobs the operator is actually employed by the crash victims, whose motor insurance companies are understandably loth to pay more than they have to. The recovery operator may still be justifying the actions he took months before, at least partly under instruction from authority, on some nearly forgotten dark and stormy night. Recovery is no occupation for the faint-hearted.

It is, however, very much a way of life for determined and resourceful men — and some women too, although not many, and those in the main introduced to it by way of family businesses. Not surprisingly many recovery operators have family histories in the motor trade, and as a result their recovery operations have become flourishing and virtually independent parts of dealerships or repair shops. Perhaps more discovered their aptitude for recovery while working for someone else, and decided to set up in business for themselves. Not a few discovered the fascination of recovery while serving in the army, while several sailors — naval and mercantile — have, in a manner of speaking, swallowed the ground anchor.

The distinguishing mark of recovery men everywhere is self-reliance coupled with an independent cast of mind, and an apparent imperviousness to heat, cold and discomfort. Their offices and cabs are usually grossly overheated, they turn out without hesitation at night and in the depths of winter, and while floundering about in the dark have learnt to distinguish between mud and water by a simple formula — mud stays outside of your boots, water gets inside!

The people are tough resourceful characters, and so are their machines. Only recently has there been much of a need for recovery vehicles that could effortlessly cruise at motorway speeds over thousands and thousands of miles, and so for the first half-century of motor traffic almost any time-expired old chassis would do, provided the lump of concrete or box of broken spring leaves over its back axle was heavy enough to prevent the wheels spinning when it tightened the towing chain attached to the dumbiron of one of its younger sisters.

It was the 1939–45 war and the armed peace which followed that effectively finished that era of recovery, for not only did those events produce large numbers of men trained in good, sound, recovery techniques but they also provided, in the 'government surplus' sales, large numbers of thoroughly well-designed and well-built wreckers.

The two factors came together, and for one reason or another the supply of army trained people and army surplus equipment did not dry up until the 1960s. Indeed there is a trickle of both, still.

There is hardly a recovery operator in the country who does not become just a little misty-eyed when conversation turns to the Diamond-Ts, Austin Westerns, Ward LaFrances, Matadors and Scammell coffeepots of old. Not a few, with only a little prompting, will open up garage doors and reveal the hoary old warrior with which they, or their fathers, set up business in Civvy Street, so long ago. Very often too it turns out that the old-timer is still a valued member of the working fleet, and is not infrequently called out when jobs requiring its own special capabilities arise.

Since the chassis of most modern heavy wreckers are not expected to become high mileage machines, and since the required dimensions and specifications are not likely to be matched by any maker's standard products, there is a strong incentive to adapt premium quality but time-served, and therefore relatively cheap, artic tractors for recovery work. Provided the finished vehicles are not capable of being used for anything but their new role in life, owners can build for themselves specials which include everything that fancy and experience dictates. Chassis frames lengthened and braced, high capacity rear axles, stiffer springing — perhaps, a little adventurously, even air suspension, which has characteristics well suited to recovery — gearboxes with plenty of ratios for coping with motorway cruising or super-low speed manoeuvring. Big lofty cabs to give good vision all round, bodywork with plenty of locker space for all the essential odds and ends that any self-respecting recoveryman cannot do without. If the equipment is going to be twin-boom then that may be secondhand as well; transferred probably from a chassis that has reached the end of its particular road.

Then of course comes the paint job, and quite clearly there is something about recovery that brings out an overwhelming urge in owners and crews to make the vehicles as handsome as possible. A few, it is true, go too far and produce fairground-like decorative effects that look quite unsuitable for attendance at the scene of an accident, but most units are clean, neat, and look well kept, with not too much polished aluminium and stainless steel about their exhaust stacks and front bumpers. Will a client, already gloomy at the prospect of large bills to be met for expensive work on his vehicle, be cheered up by the sight of a handsome and purposeful-looking recovery unit towing it in — or will he instinctively feel that anything as big and gaudy as that is going to give rise to extortionate charges? Maybe from the commercial point of view there is a nice balance for recoverymen to strike between pride of possession and customer relations.

In contrast to the heavy wreckers, car lift and tow recovery units spend most of their time on the road running up huge mileages, and so secondhand chassis usually turn out to be not much of a bargain. Apart from engines and transmissions already being worn there is also a strong likelihood that rust is eating into not very robust chassis, underframes and cabs. Whether transporters are built on to new or secondhand chassis depends very much upon the purchaser's depth of pocket, but the infinite variety of work carried out by light goods chassis during their first ownership means that even secondhand ones can be low mileage and fit for years of reliable work in their second careers.

For some not readily apparent reason the image of the wrecking industry in America appeals to many British recovery operators, who therefore develop great urges to own American-origin vehicles — even to the extent of importing new and secondhand ones. Almost invariably these stylish machines can be guaranteed to stand out in a crowd and thereby, perhaps, justify their possession in terms of advertising for their owners. By carefully selecting vehicle model and the use that will be made of it, a proud owner can avoid Type Approval law and other complications that affect an ordinary haulier who fancies something unusual for his fleet.

Powerful allies over many years for businesses at the lighter end of the market have been, and still are, the motoring 'clubs' — traditionally the Automobile Association and the Royal Automobile Club, both of which time-honoured and very large institutions now have a host of independent commercial recovery clubs snapping at their heels. These latter, led by the National Breakdown Recovery Club, gambled on a theory that many motorists would willingly forgo the wide range of services offered by the AA and RAC in exchange for lower membership fees and a guarantee of rapid rescue from mechanical breakdowns for themselves and their vehicles. It proved to be a shrewd assessment of what ordinary motorists wanted as the gamble has certainly paid off, and to provide this basic service it was essential to build a nationwide network from hundreds of already established and independent recovery operators.

Both the AA and RAC own sizeable fleets of light recovery units and transporters, but they still trust the motor trade for much of the emergency help they can offer to their members; the independent organizations rely almost entirely on commercial operators for the services they offer. The contracts which these organizations provide are no guarantee of a steady flow of work; in the circumstances that is hardly possible, but they do provide a broad foundation on which an enterprizing light recovery business can build. Perhaps even more importantly, the clubs organize and present what is the only coherent and nationwide marketing effort on behalf of the recovery industry, light and heavy.

The club approach is also rapidly becoming a mainstay of heavy breakdown and recovery. Local garages and fleets provide the basic workload it is true, but many hauliers and coach owners have discovered the advantages of what amounts to an insurance policy which gives cover against avoidable delay for vehicles. Nothing, but nothing, sells commercial vehicles like good service back-up — indeed, no matter how good a truck or bus may be, unless there is also a service organization with a first-rate reputation behind it, users will not buy. It is not too difficult to find repair shops able and willing to carry basic spares and fit them, but arranging towing, substitute vehicles and payments is another matter. For an annual premium such organizations as Mondial, Europ Assistance, Octagon and others will, in effect, take over the worries of providing all-hours, all-year, emergency aid. They in turn need networks of recovery agents, and so rely on contracted commercial operators.

A huge advantage of these schemes is that in most of them drivers need to carry only a kind of credit card, and not the large sums in a variety of currencies that would otherwise be needed to cope with emergencies at night or on public holidays. Indeed the usual promise is that if the driver with a breakdown makes just one telephone call to a central control room, then whatever help he needs will be supplied, the bills later being rendered to his employer. Such schemes are particularly useful to vehicle importers, who sell relatively few units and whose products are best attended to by trained mechanics in a franchised dealership, and also to operators with small fleets or whose vehicles are thin on the ground — perhaps on extended journeys overseas, or a long way from base.

A surprisingly large number of operators insist on heavy vehicle crash damage and breakdowns being repaired in their own workshops or by local garages they feel they can trust, and so although the vast majority of recovery work is local some very long tows are made, even from one end of the country to the other. Recovery work of this kind has encouraged even further the introduction of under-reach units which do nothing else but on-road lift and tow. So much so, in fact, that not a few are built and spend their working lives without winches. Wreckers without winches — it wouldn't have seemed feasible, not so many years ago.

Something quite unthinkable at any time is a recovery business, large or small, which does not possess effective control and communications systems. No wrecker is earning unless it is out of the yard and gainfully employed. Since towing and minor breakdowns comprise a major part of nearly all workloads, dead mileage will eat into recovery profits just as it does in any other transport business. But skilful controllers can keep vehicles busy moving from job to job, and it is noticeable that successful recovery firms often have more than one depot in an area, or working agreements with other local firms, so that their controllers can juggle work loads to maximum advantage. It follows that every vehicle must be in constant contact with base, but even with the multiplicity of communications systems that are now available, there is nothing really suitable for recovery, and overcrowded air waves create constant headaches, literally and metaphorically, for users. Two-way radio is the usual means, but the need to work through base stations which may or may not be manned, and generally poor reception, are serious drawbacks. Modern radio telephones are operationally more attractive, and add a further advantage in that drivers out on a job can make direct contact with third parties.

Compared with the huge numbers of vehicles in use on the roads, and the great mileages they cover, road traffic accidents are rarities. When they happen, the results are spectacular. Petroleum spirit tanker incidents are handled very carefully indeed.

Above *Every day in every way lorries roll over. Artics with high centres of gravity are prone to it; so are tankers. Swerving at speed is the usual reason. A rollover that left its mark — for weeks — was this full load of drums of white emulsion paint.*

Below *All buses undergo a tilt test before entering service, but when they do roll they provide a major challenge for recovery operators. The great problem is fragility and high value — it can be very easy to ruin a vehicle that would otherwise be repairable.*

Above *Although diesel fuel is not a great fire risk, there is plenty of other inflammable material in and around lorries, not including the cargoes. Usually not much can be done about fire — by the time help can arrive the vehicle is burnt out.*

Below *The comparatively light and small vehicles used by British forces in the first years of the Second World War needed only simple recovery equipment to get them out of trouble, and Scammell 'coffeepots' served in this role, among others.*

Above *The AEC Matador 4 by 4 became a classic of the 1940s and 50s. Although originally a gun tractor it was pressed in to every kind of heavy military service, including purpose-built recovery units with great winching power and luffing crane jibs.*

Below *When America entered the war it brought a new era of heavy wheeled transport, and recovery vehicles to suit. Twin-boom equipment, already widely used in the US, rapidly endeared itself to British users. Later, demobbed twin-booms found ready buyers.*

Above *Military thinking shows itself in very elaborate units. This AEC Militant had heavy winching power front and back under the chassis and along the boom, which slewed. Few civilian users could afford such a machine, except at disposal sales.*

Below *Superbly-built chassis-carrying bodywork that quickly dated meant that this Daimler was typical of many Rolls-Royces, Napiers, and others that were condemned to spend more years as garage handmaidens than they ever did as stately limousines.*

Above *An appeal that went unheard ... a farmer maddened beyond endurance by vehicles coming to grief on his land at a notorious traffic black-spot, tried without effect to dissuade trespassers. All to no avail, as the inverted artic tipper shows.*

Below *The universal law of cussedness ensures that as often as not a crashed vehicle will come to rest in a difficult location. Without the tree, recovering this Volkswagen would be straightforward; with it, damage limitation will not be easy.*

Right *Changing conditions brought changing problems, and with the pedestrian underpass came a new hazard for drivers who lose control of their vehicles — the risk of running into a stairwell. Indeed some cars have managed to get themselves well into the tunnels.*

Above left *Ever more, ever faster, traffic means that even minor errors of judgement can result in disaster, and the size of commercial vehicles increases steadily. Heavies have a good safety record, but they cause a lot of damage when they do run into trouble.*

Left *Once a moving vehicle is out of control huge destructive forces are released. Cars skidding off embankments often fly through treetops before coming to rest, presenting recovery teams with major problems. The car may be scrap, but woodland is valuable.*

Left *Until the 1960s bad weather usually had the effect of reducing the amount of traffic. But as road transport took over from railways, road vehicles continued to roll, winter and summer. Lorries and buses were getting bigger too, and their speeds increasing.*

Right *Did the skip wagon bucket fail to unhitch? Soft ground? Whatever the cause, a nasty surprise for the driver and an interesting conundrum for a recovery crew, which would be trying to get the largely undamaged lorry down without further harm.*

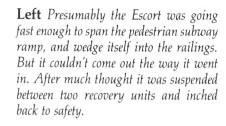

Left *Presumably the Escort was going fast enough to span the pedestrian subway ramp, and wedge itself into the railings. But it couldn't come out the way it went in. After much thought it was suspended between two recovery units and inched back to safety.*

Middle left *Car showroom with a difference! Despite having vaulted a raised flower bed and demolished the shop front, the vehicle was substantially undamaged. Even the building had escaped serious structural harm. Getting the car out called for delicate winching.*

Below *Highsided articulated tippers on exposed sites run the risk of being blown over and, when they are, standing them up again may not be an altogether straightforward task. This one is a powerful testimonial to the strength of fifth-wheel couplings.*

Right *Tanker users are a class apart — their cargoes are often lethal, their control systems and training excellent. When a vehicle does go astray the emergency services are careful indeed; only certificated recoverymen are allowed to touch hazardous goods.*

Below *Another problem with road tankers is their susceptibility to damage, coupled with high cost. Many have no chassis, and while shiny outer cladding panels may be renewable, careless recovery operations can easily dent or strain the cargo-carrying shells.*

Above *Breakdown service years ago could amount to wholesale rebuilding and agents expected to change diffs and radiators by the roadside, but these Automobile Association patrolmen of the 1920s, faced with a Foden steamer, appear to be out of their depth.*

Below *Integrally-built buses and coaches can suffer serious damage if they are lifted at either front or rear bumpers, and the only safe way to raise them is at or near an axle. Under-reach recovery units have an extending boom with locating brackets.*

Above *An ingenious home-made under-reach for limited use. Lifting a casualty vehicle at such a distance from the wrecker tailgate greatly increases the risk of overloading an axle; limited ground clearance means that booms must be both slender and stiff.*

Below *The biggest single advantage of wheel lifts for cars and light vehicles is the speed of operation, plus the fact that a single operator needs no help in moving a vehicle. Such spectacle lifts now dominate light recovery; some can be used as light cranes.*

Above *The twin-boom, still the mainstay of most heavy recovery operations world-wide after half a century. Holmes invented them, others copied them, and despite detail changes they are all very similar. The two booms are uncoupled for independent use.*

Below *Inflatable air bags are a boon in raising large vehicles quickly and with minimum damage — they show to particular advantage with buses and large vans. Usually a conventional machine is also needed to control the casualty as it comes up.*

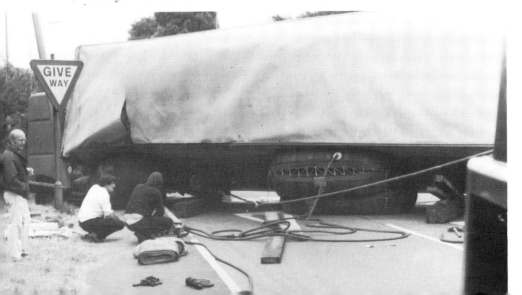

Above *The classic twin-boom wrecker, as defined by Holmes in its big 750. Their versatility ensures that such machines are still the mainstay of heavy recovery.*

Below *Wreckers International produces its Bulldog Dominator range of the time-honoured pattern. The 10, like the rest of family, can be hydraulically powered.*

Above *A Dominator 30 demonstrating its ability to pull in two directions at once. Most recovery operations depend on winching, using the booms as rope guides.*

Left *The two booms, either separately or linked, can also be rigged and used as short radius cranes. Here the casualty is also being towed.*

Left *Heart of any twin-boom — its mainframe and winches. Ropes pass upwards and are guided through swivelling fairleads to provide high level pulling.*

Above *Single-boom hydraulic units of the Century type can reduce considerably the time it takes to set up a recovery — but they lack all-round flexibility.*

Right *A casualty hitched up and ready for the road. The A-frame provides clearance and articulation, while the weight is taken by the winching ropes.*

Right *Air bags are becoming increasingly popular for righting tankers and similar easily damaged vehicles. Only low pressure air is required.*

Above *Under-reach machines are at their best in pick up and run recovery, but the addition of suitable winches turns them into generally useful units.*

Below *The cross-beam of an under-reach is adjustable, and provided with interchangeable attachments that engage with suspension mountings or axles.*

Above *The economics of vehicle recovery operation mean that most operators can justify only light vehicles for light work. So although the weights and dimensions to be handled are clearly less daunting than in heavy recovery, as much skill and guile are needed.*

Below *Fixed bed transporters are widely used to provide economical and rapid recovery for suitable vehicles. This Marquiss overcomes the problems of approach angles and low-built cars by double-sloping the deck and using long detachable ramps.*

Above *When operating conditions justify it, slideback transporters of the kind made by Brimec have their advantages, particularly for their low loading angle. Most transporters now have crew cabs fitted, for the use of the casualty car passengers.*

Below *In America, where distances to be covered can be enormous, transporters are used for commercial vehicles. For buses, with transmissions easily damaged in towing, the advantages are great. But many such movements are needed to make big transporters economic.*

Bottom *Faced with the problem of moving tracked and other vehicles unsuitable for use on public roads, military authorities have long favoured big transporters. Perhaps changing traffic conditions will persuade civilian recovery operators to adopt similar units.*

Right *One occasion when a crane proved to be the ideal tool for the job. Generally, purpose-built cranes are not particularly suitable for vehicle recovery work, for they are expensive machines and lack the winching capacity which is needed in recovery.*

Below *The equipment on recovery units is often of great use in bringing stability to precariously lodged vehicles. Badly twisted bodywork can be distorted further to help the emergency services to release trapped victims, before clearing the road.*

Above *There are sheerlegs at the front and wooden blocks underneath. No doubt two or three screw jacks are positioned on more timber, in the ditch. During the early years of the century vehicle recovery without specialized tackle presented immense difficulties.*

Below *Always hard work; often wet, cold and unpleasant into the bargain. Most recovery operators enter the business almost by chance, but despite the often tragic and uncomfortable working conditions it exercises a fascination they find hard to resist.*

Above *A curiosity among recovery vehicles — a Thornycroft Nubian airport fire tender, bought for its off-road capability and speed, and low ground weight. It is used as a mobile winch. Most operators try to incorporate maximum versatility in their machines.*

Below *Mainstay of recovery over many years — and to some extent still — the AEC Matador was cheap to buy on the surplus market, had excellent off-road capability, and plenty of power. Only recently has the call for modern lifting equipment overtaken it.*

Right *American-origin vehicles have a great fascination for British operators, some of whom are willing to spend large sums on them. Equally suitable chassis are available in Europe, but this Kenworth 6 by 4, fitted with Dyson hydraulic crane, certainly has style.*

Left *While many operators enjoy turning their own ideas into metal, purpose-built wreckers found the readiest buyers when military authorities released them on to civilian markets. Large numbers survive: some in retirement, others still working for a living.*

Left *An unlikely conversion by an enterprising engineer, this. It began as a twin-steer AEC Mammoth Minor artic tractor, modified and fitted with a Matador front axle to give four-wheel drive. The hydraulic crane and lifting equipment were also home-made.*

Right *Reasonably-dimensioned American trucks like the Mack provide a sturdy base for heavy recovery equipment, and make it possible to use winching capacity to the full. Yet their length is not excessive which is an important factor in town and country lane towing jobs.*

Right *The motoring 'clubs', still dominated by the Automobile Association and Royal Automobile Club, provide a great deal of work for recovery operators. Most own no recovery units of their own — the two giants have sizable fleets, but for breakdowns rather than crashes.*

Chapter 2

Heavy recovery

On the face of it, any recovery job seems straightforward enough. No matter how damaged the casualty vehicles may be, just get a big enough crane on site; lift the wrecks up and on to suitable transport and carry them away. And indeed a handful of jobs are done in just that manner.

For the vast majority, however, such a simple approach is not practicable. Often crashed vehicles end up in soft ground some way from any hard standing, and there is no way of reaching them without doing a great deal of damage to the surroundings. The way in which vehicles out of control can apparently vault valuable walls and hedges, somehow getting themselves into woodland, or quarries, or streams, is a constant source of amazement. Even an apparently negotiable field is probably criss-crossed with a network of fragile field drains, while the claim for compensation after, for instance, cutting up a prime golf course by ploughing across it with large vehicles would be horrific.

Something usually overlooked, too, is that a conventional crane is rated to exert its maximum capacity at a very small radius — in other words, as the boom head extends further and further out, the lifting capacity reduces dramatically. A crane capable of raising completely off the ground a disabled commercial vehicle which is placed more than a few feet from its own tailgate or sides would be a very big, very expensive machine, manned by an operator trained in lifting, not recovery, techniques. It would take a long time to travel to incidents, be unhandy in use and, most importantly, it would also lack the winching capacity which is an indispensable part of any recoveryman's repertoire. In any case, when a conventional crane of any capacity is required there will certainly be a civil engineering plant hire firm not far away who will be happy to supply whatever is wanted.

Interestingly, several recovery equipment manufacturers have adapted the principle of the hydraulically-operated telescopic crane to their own purposes, and they hold a niche in the civilian market. But these are specialist wreckers with all the ancillary equipment needed for their trade — not general purpose cranes.

A rather more obvious difficulty with any straight lift is the likelihood of considerable secondary damage being caused — even an apparent write-off may be salvable, but not if crane ropes or slings have knifed through thin body panelling. All too often, in any case, the casualty is on its side, or roof, and must at some stage in the proceedings be uprighted. That would not be easy with a machine adapted to lift rather than pull, and an added factor counting against using a conventional crane to right a rollover is that the weight to be raised can be a great deal less than it appears. Provided the casualty is lying more or less horizontally the weight to be lifted will be only about half of the total vehicle weight — the other half is carried by the casualty tyres as they bite into the ground. Of course, on an embankment where the vehicle roof is lower than its wheels the weight is a great deal more, but in general terms recovery can be said to be an exercise in damage limitation rather than mere weight shifting.

So for most jobs, instead of the brute force which the use of cranes implies, recovery experts rely instead on their winches, and a cunning born of long experience. Indeed, throughout most off-road recovery jobs the wrecker is hardly more than a secure base from which its winches can exert their seemingly irresistable pull.

For very many years — and indeed to some degree still — the lift and tow function was provided more often than not by a compact cranelike boom, wide at the base and fabricated from angle-section steel. Raising the hook and its load was achieved by hand-powered drum and cable. Nowadays these simple and trouble free machines are generally and derisively known as mangles, but there is a lot to be said for them when circumstances call for low cost equipment that will survive for years with negligible maintenance, and the vehicles to be lift-towed are also suitable and not too heavy.

However as time passed the steadily increasing size and value of casualties and the increasingly difficult surroundings in which they are likely to find themselves, coupled with the fertile imaginations of recovery operators, have given rise to any number of sound and not so sound devices for heavy lifting and recovering. In fact real needs have usually been more than met by what has become the time-honoured and much-loved twin-boom, which after half a century still more than holds its own as a universal machine.

The American Ernest Holmes corporation developed the twin-boom, and its widespread use by armies throughout the 1939–45 war — military buyers, with apparently bottomless pockets, have spent fortunes on developing, trying and discarding a huge variety of recovery equipment— thoroughly convinced transport men everywhere that Holmes had found the answer to most recovery problems. Now twin-booms are made by other companies, but the original simplicity and versatility of the Holmes concept were such that it became the definitive version, and so all twin-booms have a considerable family resemblance. Only in recent times has its dominance been challenged by fundamentally different equipment.

The basic twin-boom format is too well known to need much elaborating, although the subtleties of its design usually escape notice. On a sturdy subframe which acts also to stiffen the carrying chassis occasionally one, but far more often and more usefully two, winches are mounted near deck level in a vertical mainframe that is positioned transversely, just behind the cab. The mainframe includes two masts, each of which carries a boom which can slew from side to side. In heavier and more expensive versions the booms have telescopic extensions, and because of their size and weight these may be hydraulically operated. With the support of hand-winched top ropes the booms can also luff (although not under load), while their heads may be shackled so that the two become effectively one. Although the format looks essentially cranelike, and is indeed actually used as a crane when a casualty is being lift-towed, the real purpose of the boomheads is to act when required as high level fairleads for the winch ropes.

Not so long ago power for the winches came through a mechanical drive, with clutches, from the vehicle gearbox. Now, as in most other applications for secondary power on all kinds of vehicles, hydraulics have almost completely taken over. The resulting controllability and general operating convenience coupled with insignificant wear are huge advantages, and unlike the odd things that it could cause to happen with mechanical drives, chassis flexing under load has no effect on hydraulic pipelines. But old-time recovery men mourn the overload capacity of mechanical winches — the in-built safety factors in hydraulic systems will go so far and no further, which at least minimizes the menace of overstrained ropes. When a wire rope, stressed beyond endurance, begins to smoke — run!

Rear overhang on any wrecker is kept to the minimum, and its tailgate will incorporate a strong beam on which is hung the A-frame — a sturdy drawbar which looks just as its name suggests and which will probably have telescopic arms. These make it a bit easier to get unit and casualty properly aligned for towing. The A-frame is hinged and normally stands vertically out of the way. In use it is suspended by winch rope from the boom head, so that a casualty hitched on for towing can be raised by the rope, and kept at a safe distance from the wrecker tail by the A-frame.

Because the winches and their ropes can be used separately it is possible, indeed common, to exert simultaneous winching efforts in two different directions — one perhaps at ground level, the other anything up to 15 ft high through a boom head. This dual facility is useful when a tall casualty lying on its side is being righted — if it comes up too quickly (and a rollover usually shows great eagerness to get back on to its wheels) there is a real risk that the tyres and suspension will yield enough to bounce it over in the opposite direction. But with the second rope being paid out slowly to act as a backstay, the whole operation can be kept safely under control.

The greatest single advantage of recovery vehicles which use hydraulically extending booms is the great power they can quickly and easily bring to bear, and they certainly score when a rollover is placed in such a way that it can, through the ropes and straps harnessed to it, be 'pushed' upright. Their booms will travel in or out and luff while carrying a full load, and need only a minimum of the wire rope rigging which is so time-consuming when twin-booms are used. And this simplicity reduces by some degree the amount of skill required by operators. The fundamental difference between a recovery vehicle and a crane is that the former must be able to handle heavy loads at low heights while a crane is intended to cope with small loads at great heights. This distinction makes it possible for wrecker boom assemblies to be short, very sturdy, and to use robust components.

Superficially there are resemblances. Telescoping booms in both comprise very stiff box-section tubes, usually rectangular in section (although Wreckers International is now trying octagonal ones), with the upper sections sliding inside the lower ones on anti-friction bearings. Hydraulic rams power the inner booms in and out, and although occasionally rope-operated assemblies are still to be met, their time was both short and a long while ago. Although crane booms usually have three or more sections, wreckers almost invariably have only two. Base sections are hinged horizontally to a rotating platform in most cranes and few wreckers, and booms are raised and lowered by sometimes one but more usually two lifting rams. Again, powerful winches are an essential part of the permanent equipment on a wrecker, but with a non-slewing boom any sideways pull from the boom head may put an undesirable stress on the whole structure. Provided the machine is fitted with a large enough hydraulic pump, and most of them are these days, then an operator can use several functions simultaneously.

The limitations of a crane-style unit are illustrated by their lifting capacities — if a big one can safely handle 30 tons when its boom is fully contracted then its full reach capacity will be only 10 tons. But the biggest operating disadvantage with telescopic recovery units (their inevitably high price tags count against these machines too) is that except on the most expensive models, typically those bought by armies, the booms do not slew, so that a crashed vehicle must be in such a position that the recovery truck can approach it.

Only rarely is it possible to position any wrecker so that straight-line winching is enough. On-site complications usually make it necessary to exert the pull at awkward angles, and then the ropes have to be taken around snatch pulley blocks secured to ground anchors. Trees can make splendid anchors, on the rare occasions when they were planted in suitable positions; in their absence, long strong stakes driven deep into the ground will serve very well. Not infrequently a second recovery unit is needed to make a simultaneous pull or, maybe, to act as an anchor or restraint. A crashed vehicle, back on its wheels and quite possibly having suffered damage to its steering and brake systems, has great potential for causing further mayhem. It pays to prevent embarrassing runaways by keeping them on short leads.

If the casualty can be moved on its own wheels, all well and good. However it really is remarkable how heavy trucks can seemingly fly over impassable territory before coming to rest, thereby causing the maximum aggravation to the unfortunates who have got the job of persuading them back on to a road. It may be necessary to lay a 'corduroy' road across soft ground — old wooden railway sleepers are a godsend to recovery operators for all sorts of jobs, not least in making temporary roads. More usually the errant truck is empty and quite light, so that it can be hauled by winch across quite soft ground and fragile bridges. Once it is on any kind of firm surface the battle is nearly over. Provided there is something solid enough to hitch on to at one end or the other of the casualty, the wrecker can assume its role as a crane. With the A-frame secured, that end of the vehicle can be lifted off the ground and the convoy tidied up and made fit for the road.

Increasingly, however, there is the problem of vehicles built in such a way that they cannot be lift-towed in the time-honoured fashion. The difficulties presented by integrally constructed buses and coaches, with no chassis and only the flimsiest of framing under their floors are evident to anyone who has ever looked underneath one of them, but even the classic rigid eight-wheeler, a sturdy enough machine, can suffer terminal chassis damage if an attempt is made to lift it at the front bumper. It pays to remember that in normal circumstances all the loads on a vehicle are carried by its wheels, and in lifting from an extreme end the vehicle 'wheelbase' is effectively lengthened by the distance between hook and centre of the nearest axle. The chassis frame (which at any time is no more than a simple bridge carried on supports) is not made strongly enough to withstand the effect of moving its supports much further apart. So it bends at the weakest point, usually just behind the cab.

Not only long wheelbase eight-leggers are liable to damage in this way. Often the cargo inside a partially loaded four-wheeler will be shot forward against the front bulkhead as the vehicle comes to a violent halt. Hanging meat is a prime offender and when, like meat, the cargo will probably be spoiled by unloading it before recovery, attempts to lift the still laden vehicle are likely to result in the gap between back of cab and front of body rapidly closing.

In such cases disaster may be averted by bracing the chassis frame so that it can absorb the unnatural stresses being placed on it. Usually this is best done by running chains from end to end, one underneath each side-member, and putting timber spacers between chains and frame to form classic 'queen trusses' reminiscent of the bracings to be seen underneath older railway carriages, where they serve an exactly similar purpose. Some care has to be taken by recovery operators, while in all probability lying on their backs in mud, to find secure anchorages for their chains and to ensure that they are tensioned enough, but not too much, and to make sure that they won't harm any chassis components — some of which may well have been pushed out of position in the crash. Off the road, in a ditch, and/or on its side, a large vehicle is already undergoing a great deal of stress, and it is well to get it chained up before attempting any move that may cause damage. Properly braced, the risk is considerably reduced.

Any wrecker applies its lift and tow effort at a point behind its rear axles, and while this overhang is always kept to a minimum it still has the effect of turning the unit into a see-saw, with the rearmost axle as fulcrum. And this, naturally enough, has the effect of trying to lift the front wheels off the ground, an awkward phenomenon, since the front wheels should exert at least 25 per cent of the braking effort. So although the handiest kind of heavy duty recovery unit would be very short in overall length there is a need to provide satisfactory counterbalance, and the easiest way of doing so is to lengthen the wheelbase.

Occasionally, for casual use, a time-served articulated tractor has some kind of lifting device mounted on its back. Apart from permanently fitted light cranes, a few makers supply fifth-wheel attachments which provide a secure means of hitching on to and raising A-frames.

These devices, made by Steiner, Holmes, TFL and others, can be quickly fitted and removed and are a convenient way of recovering vehicles that are not too heavy. Indeed any artic tractor chassis is really suitable only for use as a ballasted tug, and typically its lift and tow capacity is limited largely to others of its own kind.

That is all very well, but most kinds of commercial vehicles are approaching what must be their maximum practicable lengths, and some are very long indeed. This means the overall train length of a twin-boom wrecker and its burden can easily reach 75 ft or more, and become a perfect nuisance in traffic and while manoeuvring. The need for a fairly lengthy working clearance between wrecker tail and casualty, to allow sharp turns to be made, makes matters worse.

At first sight it looks as though, whatever their other advantages, under-reach recovery units do little to reduce the manoeuvring problems caused by train length. The under-reach owes all its early development to Swedish manufacturers, notably Eka who began to perfect it during the 1960s, and later Bro, but more recently the British Wreckers International and TFL concerns have taken a lead in pushing the concept forward.

There are some interesting design problems to be overcome in designing under-reach units. Not least of them is the very tight clearance under modern buses and coaches, particularly when their air suspensions have deflated. The main part of the lifting boom, inboard of the wrecker, can be as deep and stiff as needs be, and its hydraulic rams have a pretty easy job compared to those fitted to excavators and other sorts of construction plant. But the slender outer end must be made with minimum depth so that it can be inserted under a coach — not that there is a lot of clearance under any axles these days. In addition this outer beam is usually arranged to fold upwards out of the way when not in use, and it really must be made to telescope. So high duty alloy steels have to be used, and in designing it the calculations must be very carefully made, if the thing isn't going to bend in use, or at least become so flexible as to be useless.

At the extremity of the beam is a centrally pivoted crosshead bar, the ends of which are fitted with pairs of interchangeable forks that actually engage an axle or other carrying points. In addition to all the other problems they present to recoverymen the undersides of modern buses and coaches are a maze of pipes and cables which make it very difficult to find suitable lifting locations, and so users need as much versatility as the equipment makers can devise. What is essential is remote control of the boom movements — the only way to be sure of causing no damage to a vehicle is to lie there underneath it, hoping its air suspension will stay inflated for just a little longer, and with extension lead switch in hand controlling precisely just where the lifting forks are placed.

It is the pivot pin which becomes the articulation point for an under-reach unit and its casualty. Clearly the whole assembly has to be very sturdy and capable also of applying a lifting force of perhaps 5 tons when fully extended. This doesn't sound much, but it is enough to cope with most vehicles.

Because of the way in which it works, the loadings are applied to it at a considerable distance behind the rearmost axle, and with one side of the see-saw so long and heavily weighted, a lengthy wheelbase is needed to provide counterbalance. In spite of this the under-reach method of working is actually a big help in increasing manoeuvrability, because what happens is that the articulation point of the wrecker-casualty train moves from the front of the casualty (at the point where it would otherwise be linked to an A-frame) to the axle which is being lifted. Indeed, the further back that axle is, the better — from the handling point of view, at any rate. It is also practicable to reduce clearance between the two vehicles to a seemingly impossible minimum and, equally usefully, trailer cut-in on bends is much less too.

In some heavy flat-tow jobs it is possible to dispense with the services of a second driver or steersman by using lifting beams instead. These beams are suitably cranked box-section girders, from 6 ft to 10 ft long, and they are used in pairs. Each has one end suitably shaped to fit over the casualty axle, and they are long enough to project beyond its bodywork, forming in effect an extension of the casualty vehicle chassis that can be hitched to any wrecker A-frame. Provided the appropriate axle is so securely chained up that its springs are out of action, and provided the vehicle chassis or floor framing can withstand the upward pressure imposed by the beams, and provided that where necessary the chassis is braced from end to end with tensioned chains, a safe suspended tow can be made. The biggest single advantage of lifting beams is their low cost, but by extending the point of lift well forward of the casualty front panelling they may also save some insurance claims for secondary damage caused while towing.

In such an unpredictable occupation as vehicle recovery, operators have an understandable instinct to include as much versatility as possible in their equipment — it is hard to imagine anything that might not come in handy at some time or another. On a rather grander scale than the odds and ends that are normally thought of in the 'potentially useful' category are attempts to combine in one machine the versatility needed for heavy off-road recovery, and the ease and rapidity of operation that is wanted to cope with modern breakdown lift-towing.

Twin-booms are still the mainstay of many, if not most, companies, and since these units are tough enough to outlast two or three chassis there is a great reluctance to part with them. Wreckers International, appreciating this, has therefore designed a version of its heavy duty hydraulically operated under-reach that can be fitted to the chassis under a twin-boom, so that either sets of equipment can be out of use without materially affecting operations with the other.

That is one approach. Another is to combine in one unit an hydraulic telescopic crane and an under-reach — the latter in the form of a extension to the main boom, cranked down, and also hydraulically operated. Ty-Rite, Wreckers International, Roger Dyson, Holmes, and other makers of crane-style recovery units sell them. This is a fairly obvious combination of functions, but it does have the drawback that it would be very difficult to make the boom slew. Another snag is first cost, for most operators reckon that towing comprises an overwhelming proportion of their workload, which implies that the crane part would not see much use, for, such is the nature of things that when the crane function is wanted urgently in one place, the wrecker will probably be miles away, using its under-reach on a straightforward towing job.

The Holmes concern, understandably keen to maximize the goodwill built up by its twin-boom machines, takes the mainframe and winch assemblies of these units as the bases for a family of remarkably sturdy hydraulic cranes. Each single extension crane boom is in the shape of a heavily braced letter T, with the cross-piece of the T forming a horizontal hinge across the mainframe; the boom is raised and lowered by means of a pair of rams. Slewing obviously isn't possible, but this format still allows the winch cables to emerge from the mainframe top, so that they can exert maximum pull to either side or to the rear, independently of the boom. These Holmes hybrids are powerful — the biggest has a rated winching capacity of 40 tons.

For many off-road recovery jobs the old-style skills and guile needed to get an overturned vehicle back on to its wheels are gradually being replaced by the somewhat easier techniques of using air bags. Air bags, although long established in rescuing aeroplanes without causing additional damage, are recent introductions to vehicle recovery and expensive, so their full potential is still being explored. But there are some distinct structural similarities between aeroplanes and modern, tender-skinned, road tankers — and the tankers may very well be filled with thousands of gallons of lethal or inflammable substances. Since it may not be possible to remove all the contents, including potentially highly dangerous vapour, prudent recovery operators handle tankers, whether full or apparently empty, very carefully indeed. Although far less likely to put a whole district at risk, the structures of big panel vans are also thin-skinned and tender, and if avoidable damage during recovery is indeed avoided (remembering to close and lock any doors, especially at the back, does a lot to keep down claims) then customers will be pleased. In such cases, and others, air bags are proving to be a boon.

Their dimensions can be whatever is wanted within reason, but generally useful ones measure 4 ft square by 5 ft to 7 ft high, inflated. They are made of heavily reinforced and very tough nylon reinforced neoprene rubber, and while sharp edges can cut or damage them, air bags stand up well to the hazards of recovery use. Typically three, four, or five would be needed to right a large vehicle — using several will spread the load and minimize stress on the casualty.

The bags operate at low pressures — about 7 psi maximum, for 1 psi produces about 1 ton of jacking force — and require only a small portable compressor to supply the volume of air required. A control console is necessary for balancing rates of inflation, and for generally keeping tight control of the operation during a lift and, just as important, deflation under load, whether expected or sudden. Since nothing in this world is perfect there can be some risk in using air bags — a blow-out in one may put an instant overload on the others, and there is a possibility that as a vehicle begins to rise, and the load on the bags begins to lessen, one may lose its grip and pop out.

Almost invariably air bags can be used to perform only the first stage of an uprighting exercise and once the casualty is well off the ground a conventional winch machine can take over and complete the job, for by then the force to be exerted is not great. Winching power is needed anyway to steady the vehicle as it rises, and to prevent uncontrolled and too-rapid movement. When it is an articulated lorry that has to be stood up again the bags are placed under the trailer body, for as that rises the tractor will follow. The fifth-wheel coupling is well able to stand the strain, and in a first-class operation tractor and trailer will be rigged so as to form, effectively, one vehicle. On those too-frequent occasions when a fifth-wheel pin has not been secured before the tractor moved off, an air bag or two can be just the thing for raising the front end of a kneeling semi-trailer without damaging it further.

One modern form of lorry bodywork which often resists air bag lifting is the curtainsider, for all the air bags can do is press against the load, ultimately pushing it right through. A lot depends on the cargo of course: in some circumstances the load can be taken out by hand but often traffic authorities refuse point-blank to allow any such time-consuming procedures. Up it must come, all in one piece, and quickly. Then a co-ordinated operation with bags lifting the load and a wrecker lifting the vehicle will probably answer.

Another useful sphere of action is in retrieving the lorry which is lying on its side under a low bridge. Repeated road resurfacings may well have made the declared clearance under the bridge a snare and delusion, and not many lorry drivers know to the inch the overall height of their vehicles. Taken at speed the sudden blow makes the lorry unstable and over it goes, with still enough momentum on it to slide the whole thing forward, under the bridge. Skip wagons and truck-mounted concrete mixers, both with high centres of gravity, seem to be particularly prone to this kind of mishap, and since the mixer drum will probably be worth more than the chassis on which it is mounted, the owners won't approve of winching the thing clear, still on its side. There is never enough headroom for a conventional wrecker to work, and so this can become another kind of job where air bags more than justify their cost.

To the uninitiated it is surprising how willing to get back on to its wheels the average lorry or bus proves to be, but in most ordinary formations the centre of gravity is quite low and even a double-decked bus, fully loaded upstairs and empty in the lower saloon, is required to lean over to at least 28° from the vertical before it shows signs of toppling. In fact it is far more difficult, when a demonstration is being staged, to make a large vehicle lay down — something which gives the thoughtful onlooker cause to ponder about the enormous forces that are unleashed in any crash.

The very low operating pressures required for air bags means that in cases of dire emergency a single small one can be inflated from a vehicle exhaust pipe. In such circumstances, of course, accurate control isn't practicable — but carefully harnessed with chain to a distorted body or cab shell, such a bag may be able to straighten it sufficiently to release a trapped person.

Air bags were not long in use before it became clear that there was a major snag in getting them properly placed before being able to upright a big vehicle that was lying on its side. Fully collapsed, a bag is still some 2 in thick — and they are awkward weighty things to manhandle. On soft ground some sort of trench can be dug to give a bag a start, but on paved surfaces that can't be done. (Before pulling a vehicle upright by winch it is usually possible, somehow, to get a flat strap underneath it.) The answer was starter mats, envelopes only $\frac{1}{2}$ in thick deflated, and which can always be inveigled under a corner of an overturned vehicle to lift it enough to give its big brothers a fair start. A more recent refinement is the angled air bag, still square in plan, but with top and bottom forming a wedge shape so that the bag fits more securely under a partly raised vehicle.

Air bag recovery can be quick and easy, but less obvious advantages stem from the low pressure and large surface areas for, providing there are no sharp stones or sapling stumps to hole them, nothing more than a sheet of plywood need be laid on the ground, and probably not even that, to form a base. And while obviously the underside of any vehicle that has rolled over and slid along is already damaged, at least air bags will do no further harm. They can indeed bear on the windows of a bus without cracking them. A fascinating additional function is to provide buoyancy for vehicles that have ended up in deep water. Suitable bags inserted into a submerged car or coach — or submerged boat — can be inflated and remotely controlled to give just the flotation needed.

When straightforward craneage is essential to extricate a heavy vehicle, the machinery required can be formidable. In this instance two very large lorry-mounted units were needed — as much for controllability as for their combined lifting power.

Above *Another of the occasions when a straightforward lift by a conventional crane had its advantages. The circumstances were such that the minimum of obstruction to other road users would be caused, and the least damage to a valuable mixer drum.*

Below *Purpose-built unit of the early 1920s. The jib is fixed, with hand-operated single chain for lifting — a lot of heavy hand work would be needed to recover an off-road casualty. The chassis is a Halley — chain final drive was stronger than live axles for towing.*

Above *When the Mersey Tunnel opened in 1934 this Leyland Beaver went to work. The hand-powered rotating crane, which also luffed, was built by Herbert Morris. On the deck are two dollies for carrying immobilized casualties. By modern standards the overhang is excessive.*

Below *Simple fixed cranes were adequate for most light and medium recovery until the modern era of easily damaged panelwork. By 1939, when this Austin was commissioned, recovery vehicle appearance was beginning to matter too, at least to publicity-conscious dealerships.*

Left *Give them a sturdy but cheap chassis, with low-cost equipment to put on it, and anyone could afford their own wrecker. But modern recovery needs are moving away from the attractive simplicity of this elderly ERF and its Harvey Frost crane and hand-winch.*

Right *Ford Transcontinental with Wreck-Master twin-boom, demonstrating its high level winching capacity in extracting a loaded tipper from soft ground. The booms are idle, leaving the winches to give an inclined pull that helps to lift the vehicle free.*

Left *First, 1920s, thoughts on the twin-boom. The only significant subsequent change was to close-couple the boom-heads in place of the cross-bar shown here. Each boom is hinged and can luff; in addition, it can slew outwards. Forward braces resist loadings.*

Below left *Arrangement of the classic twin-boom. Heart of the unit is the mainframe behind the cab, with its winches. The ropes from these rise vertically through the frame and emerge on top — either to run back over the boomheads, or independently, as needed.*

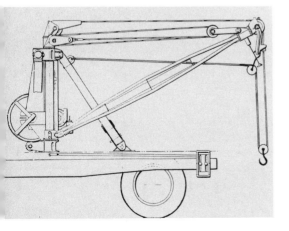

Right *With their independently controlled winches twin-boom wreckers can pull in two directions simultaneously. This ability is particularly useful in manoeuvring a casualty — a touch on one control lever, so, ease off the other a little, and out she comes ...*

Above *An American-made Holmes 850 twin-boom, fitted in Britain to a Leyland chassis for export to Kuwait. The 850 is a heavy unit — US rating on the winches is 40 tons lift — but since this machine is in general use it also has car-towing slings fitted at the back.*

Left *Glamour, American style. This Kenworth, imported second-hand into Britain complete with its Holmes 750 equipment, was completely refurbished and fitted with a Wreckers International under-reach. A useful accessory is the telescopic tower-mounted floodlight.*

Left *The A-frame is securely chained to something solid under the front end of the casualty, and then its weight can be taken on the hooks and cable. Since the frame has telescopic arms, even a badly distorted vehicle can be properly aligned with the wrecker.*

Above *By using two machines a roll-over can be put back on to its feet with small risk of sustaining further damage. In this instance air bags assisted by a twin-boom have raised the tanker, while the under-reach winch is paying out rope to form a backstay.*

Below *An attribute of the powered telescopic boom is its ability to exert considerable force in a straight line, enabling it to push or, in this instance of a Maintruck RS 2000 righting a tanker, to pull. Non-slewing machines need lining up with the job.*

Above *Business end of the Foden Recoverer. An advantage in uncomplicated jobs is the absence of ropes and pulleys needing to be rigged. For winching, the boom head acts as a fairlead, and snatch pulley blocks can be hung from the forged eyes on the tailgate.*

Below *Single boom recovery vehicles for civilian use followed well behind those built for armies and are less versatile, but in practice that hardly matters. An export specification Foden chassis forms a suitable base for this Wreckers International Recoverer.*

Above *Compared to the Foden, this ex-service AEC Militant with Reynolds Boughton superstructure is replete with elaborations — six-wheel drive, cross-country tyres, heavy winching capacity under the chassis, luffing and slewing boom, and much beside.*

Below *The Militant in action. With its hydraulically operated stabilizers lowered, the chassis becomes a solid base, allowing the crane jib to work without risk at full capacity. Like all cranes, maximum lift is at a small radius from the machine.*

Above *In addition to its hydraulically extended and raised boom, the Leyland-mounted Maintruck has considerable winching power. Rear overhang is kept to a minimum, and a heavy duty ground anchor, hinged up for travelling, can be lowered when needed.*

Below *Leyland began delivery of these 6 by 6 recovery units in 1962, long before civilian operators could buy equivalent machines. The superstructure swivelled through almost a full circle, crane movements being controlled by an operator seated by the boom.*

Above right *The British army still favours multi-purpose telescopic cranes for much of its recovery work, and it has taken into service a number of Scammell 6 by 6 chassis with Reynolds Boughton superstructures. Good cross-country mobility is regarded as essential.*

Middle right *Unspectacular things, ground anchors, but invaluable. Flat steel bars are linked together, and through prepunched holes long spikes are driven. Enough links and enough spikes will give a firm grip in almost any soil, providing a reliable anchor for snatch blocks.*

Below *Given a suitable tractor, and a genuine breakdown, there is some latitude in legal limits on the overall length of a road train. Practical considerations, however, prompt cautious operators to take really awkward loads no further than necessary, to a place of safety.*

Left *With no modification to the tractor, detachable recovery units like this Holmes can be mounted on the fifth-wheel plate. Casualties are chained up in the usual way to the spreader bar, and then self-contained hydraulic rams can raise the load for travelling.*

Right *An Interstater taking shape on a lengthened Renault in the Wreckers International workshops shows how a separate subframe is mounted on top of the chassis. The main boom pivot is well forward, and a massive ground anchor is incorporated at the rear.*

Right *Clearance is tight under modern passenger vehicles ... Remote control makes it possible for an operator lying underneath to position the crosshead of his under-reach. Interchangeable forks that engage with axles, chassis, or spring hangers, are used.*

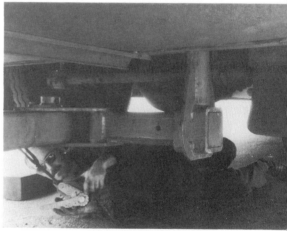

Left *The Swedish Eka company was a pioneer of under-reach recovery equipment for heavy vehicles, but others soon began to copy them. In this Eka the boom can be raised high enough to double as a crane — a separate winch is housed behind the Foden's front bumper.*

Right *Full extension is needed before an under-reach can pick up at a suitable point on long overhang buses and coaches. Boom design is therefore critical and so too, very often, is the matter of maximum loads and overloads on the recovery vehicle rear axle.*

Left *A big advantage of the under-reach is the way in which it reduces to a minimum the clearance necessary between towing vehicle and casualty. As a result the trailer cuts in far less than it would with a conventional hitch, and tighter corners can be negotiated.*

Below and bottom *A 1960s approach to recovery by under-reach. The Mersey tunnel authority commissioned this large Boss fork truck. It could lift either end of a loaded lorry off the road and, since the cab had dual controls, the unit could move at full speed forward or backward.*

Right *An unexpected sort of recovery problem, and one that would probably respond best to treatment by a large crane — with a stronger trailer.*

Below *The classic army machine, in civilian service. Leyland chassis with a slewing crane controlled by an operator seated on the superstructure.*

Left *Another military unit that found ready buyers at disposal sales — the American origin Diamond T, prized for its winching capacity.*

Left *A particularly welcome attribute of spectacle lift recovery units is their ability to work in congested streets and car parks.*

Below *Long-distance towing in the United States has created a breed of huge and beautifully maintained recovery trucks. Peterbilts are favoured chassis.*

Right *Another Peterbilt. The under-reach took some time to establish itself in America, but now this type of equipment is rapidly growing in popularity.*

Right *A Kenworth in full West Coast style and carrying twin-boom equipment. Another transatlantic exile in Britain, it looks almost too glamorous to use.*

Below *Fixed bed transporters are a low cost means of making all wheels off the ground recovery, something encouraged by vehicle licensing law.*

Left *Recovery with clean hands and no overalls is possible with a slide bed — an important point when moving new vehicles or rental cars.*

Below *So many breakdowns have to be recovered from continental Europe that the traffic justifies the use of full-size car transporters.*

Right *Damage-free recovery for vehicles with 'soft' or fragile front panelling can be achieved by using lifting beams. They are hitched over the casualty axle, and effectively form extensions to its chassis. Then a conventional lift can be made.*

Below *Traditional twin-booms seem not to wear out, and so a practicable way of combining their advantages with those of more recent developments is, on suitable chassis, to add a quite separate underreach. In this example the towing A-frame can be dismantled.*

Above *Holmes has sought to combine the advantages and reputation of its twin-boom machines with those of hydraulic cranes. It keeps the mainframe and winches of the former, with top exits for the ropes, adding a single telescopic jib that can act as fairleads.*

Below *The Holmes Lancer, demonstrating its prowess in a straightforward crane lift. Only one winch is needed for such a light load, leaving the other free to provide any necessary guidance or assistance, by pulling through ground anchored snatch blocks.*

Above *Air bags are bidding fair to dominate a great deal of straightforward roll-over work, and whatever is thereby lost in the way of traditional winching skills will be more than compensated by speed of operation and reduction in further damage to casualties.*

Below *Earlier days and earlier ways. What was alleged to be the only roll-over by a Reading Corporation trolleybus, being righted in the 1950s. On the left are the pair of hand jacks used to give an initial lift: no restraint to control bouncing is visible.*

Above left *Demonstrating the traditional London Transport method of righting a double-decker bus, with the recovery vehicle to the extreme right exercising its winching power through an anchored snatch block. A rail on the ground prevents the tyres skidding as the bus comes up.*

Middle left *Damage limitation in the overturned London Transport RT. Specially adapted screw-adjusted braces are installed in the upper saloon: they will resist lozenging when the ropes that are to be passed through the open windows and over the roof begin to tighten.*

Below *Low bridges seem to have a fatal fascination for too-high vehicles, and bridges built on the skew are much inclined to turn over lorries that hit them. When they do, inertia causes the truck to slide forward. Prime victims are mobile concrete mixers.*

Above *In this sad instance the under-bridge roll-over crushed a car, adding to the confusion. In most cases the only practicable solution is to drag the casualty clear by main force and a powerful winch — there is no headroom for a conventional operation.*

Below *Skip wagons too are prone to hitting bridges and rolling. It is another class of incident where air bags can be invaluable. Provided there is enough clearance overhead for the vehicle to be stood upright, air bags may be a neat and effective solution.*

Above *One of the very few attempts to build a vehicle specifically for recovery was made by Wreckers International, but it remained a prototype. Conventional lorry chassis are readily modified for recovery use, with an advantage in first price and maintenance costs.*

Below *Heavy duty transporters have long been used for moving civil engineering plant and similar equipment, but there is little sign yet of commercial recovery firms in Britain adopting them. The Brimec slideback system is well adapted to loading medium-weight lorries.*

Chapter 3

Light recovery

Since passenger cars are both light and compact they are not, on the whole, liable to cause such perplexing recovery problems as heavy commercial vehicles. In any case, a crash-damaged car probably has little residual value. However because there are so many more cars than there are coaches and lorries, and because they usually travel much faster, and because their drivers are overwhelmingly less experienced or competent, cars are much more frequently involved in traffic incidents, and often end up in unbelievable predicaments.

As one would expect the rates that can be charged for recovering a car are rather less than those for heavier vehicles, and so it is not economic to have heavy wreckers on standby for car-based incidents. In any case, most car breakdowns involve recovering not just the vehicle but its passengers and their luggage, for which purpose not even the most glamorous of heavy wreckers is suitable. Recovery units for car work are, therefore, usually based on a format which keeps their gross weight below the magic. 7.5 tonnes mark, above which drivers in Britain must hold heavy goods vehicle driving licences, and indeed many vehicles don't exceed 3.5 tonnes, another convenient legal dividing line. Traditionally heavier versions of the Ford Transit, a classic design if ever there was one, were favoured by most equipment makers and users. In addition, maximum capacity Freight Rover Sherpas are making inroads, and the Dodge 50 series is favoured too. For the slightly heavier machines, chassis in the small Ford Cargo, Bedford TL and Dodge Commando class are liked. From all of which it may be inferred that price, reliability, and familiarity are prime factors when it comes to choosing the chassis for a light recovery vehicle.

There is also a real need for units capable of coping with off-road conditions and for many years, in the days when hand-operated wreckers were not thought to be beneath the dignity of image-conscious recoverymen, the Land Rover, with Harvey Frost, TFL or

Dixon Bate crane on its back, stood supreme, on and off the road. But Land Rover axle loadings were conservatively rated to combat military-style rough terrain work, and therefore appeared to be too low for suspended-towing — something of small concern for a long time, but a factor that took on real significance once police forces began to look closely at equipment used by the recovery companies they called out to traffic accidents. However once the vehicle had been re-rated by its makers for recovery work it came back into favour, particularly now its traditional jib cranes, hand-powered or electric, have been joined by hydraulically-operated spectacle frames.

A distinct attribute of the traditional cranes is their great versatility. Apart from the standard slings and chains, which make it possible for them to cope with almost any car-sized vehicle that is possessed of a reasonably sturdy bumper and not too much damage-prone panelling and trim beneath the bumper, their makers also produce special lifting frames. These are tailored to fit underneath individual models, and make it possible for them to be raised and towed damage-free, but of course fitting and removing them takes rather longer than pushing a spectacle frame into place and lifting it. An incidental advantage with these self-contained cranes is the ease with which they can be quickly mounted on and removed from any of a wide range of light pick-ups. The vehicles can therefore be kept busy when their recovery function is not in demand and, rather more usefully, the long-lasting cranes can, as the years go by, be easily moved to replacement vehicles.

While British operators, generally, can be said to have moved from hand (or light power) cranes directly to damage-free under-reaches for car recovery, American operators have always had to face the problems created by longer, wider and heavier passenger cars — and a sizable population of panel vans and large pick-ups. The difficulties these pose when it comes to getting accident-damaged strays back on to a road and then towing them over long distances are well beyond the capabilities of simple light equipment, and so distinctively American breeds of light recovery units have evolved, using chassis of around the $4\frac{1}{2}$ tons gross vehicle weight mark. Over the years, and understandably, the twin-boom format has taken pride of place in Holmes thinking and its smallest machine, based on twin 4 ton winches, is almost a scale model of those with five times its rated capacity. 'Small' in such things is a relative term, for provided the operator knows what he is doing when he rigs the ropes, snatch blocks and anchors, the results from winches of apparently low capacity can equal or surpass those from much bigger units that are less cleverly used. Since they are real twin-booms, these smaller machines are capable of all the many functions common to their breed. There is an incidental bonus in that the generally compact dimensions of their chassis and equipment makes the machines suitable for use as handy and versatile over the side cranes for lifting and placing heavy pieces of machinery, or vehicle components.

In a logical progression from these classic designs users in this sector of the market have taken to their hearts purpose-built telescopic cranes, for in run-of-the-mill light recovery the great versatility of twin-booms is only rarely used to full capacity. On the other hand the speed with which an hydraulic crane can be rigged and got to work is money in the bank to any owner, and their lifting capacities of between 3 to 8 tons on a closed boom and up to 3 tons fully extended find willing buyers for the products of Century, Holmes, Wreckers International, and others.

To a degree the lack of twin-boom flexibility in use is more apparent than real with these units, for by mounting the boom-head sheave or pulley in a suitable swivel the rope can be led out in any direction — even, on low-built chassis, over the wrecker cab roof. There is, however, always the risk of damaging the boom by a too-enthusiastic sideways pull. With hydraulic power already available there is little difficulty in increasing the versatility of these recovery units even further by adding spectacle lifts, and they are usually optional fittings.

The attraction of things American for British recoverymen certainly extends to the lighter end of the market, and when dollar-pound exchange rates lean in the appropriate direction small numbers of machines are imported complete, ready for use. This enthusiasm is spurred by the availability in western Europe generally of equipment sold off as time-expired by American military forces. In common with most 'army surplus', careful buying can produce excellent bargains — whether new or secondhand, the distinctive appearance and styling of American light trucks and equipment is eyecatching, and certainly draws the attention of passers-by to garages which own them, and are bright enough to stand them prominently on a forecourt.

When cars had chassis and their four wheels were positioned at the corners, lift-tows gave no cause for anxiety, no cause at all. A simple jib, a simple hand-operated winch, an old tyre or seat cushion to act as buffer between the two vehicles, was enough. But as front and rear overhangs increased on cars so too did the risk of overstraining body structures by lifting at the extreme front or rear — because just as in the case of modern integral buses, to do so increases the distance between supports for the load. And so, again just like the 'soft' commercial vehicles, the most sensible course is to lift a car from its wheels, and there is a growing inclination on the part of makers to state that they approve lifting only at the wheels. There is certainly a marked difference in approach by operators who habitually tow repairable vehicles, and those who specialize in cars whose day is done — the former avoid cranes and slings; the latter use hardly anything else.

In getting the wheels of a light casualty off the ground two distinct avenues are available — a crane-like wrecker can be used to hoist from above, or something bearing a close resemblance to the heavy duty under-reach can lift from below. For general purpose car recovery there is a lot to be said for machines like the splendidly-named Cradle Snatcher, made by Vulcan in Canada, and in similar forms by several other firms. An extra supplied with this telescopic hydraulic crane is a spreader bar to be suspended on its hook, and strong straps dropping down to ground level where they support a frame that engages the wheels. This outfit can easily raise one axle of any car. However when there is enough lift and tow work available to keep a recovery unit fully occupied the so-called damage-free or spectacle lifts undoubtedly come into their own. Sterling efforts by Ty-Rite and Brimec during the early 1980s at gaining acceptance for this idea have now reaped the inevitable reward of many imitators, and obscure the earlier efforts of others who were before their time.

However, these devices are now the common currency of lift and tow light recovery in Britain — the motoring organizations alone own hundreds — and although several makers compete fiercely their products are all very similar, with a rearward-projecting boom, capable of some vertical movement and hydraulically powered, which has at its outer end a swept down tail section. This carries an open frame that can be laid flat on the road, and even a little below nominal road surface when occasion demands; it is shaped to fit around each wheel, and from its appearance is known inevitably as a spectacle frame — more rarely and less convincingly as a butterfly, or a whale-tail.

These units are so quick and easy for one-man operation that they are frequently used to move even perfectly fit cars for whom second drivers are not available — 'one-way' car hire companies, faced with accumulations of abandoned cars at airports and railway stations, often make use of this one-man recovery. Eagle, an American make, has gone further along this path by devising self-engaging wheel frames, so that an operator doesn't even have to leave his cab except, presumably, on those occasions when a handbrake is to be released.

An obvious and inevitable advance in the spectacle lift theme is to make the two wheel frames detachable, and to plant removable axle-stand jaws on the short crossbar that remains. The result is a passing imitation of the full size under-reach, for the machine can then find several places to engage underneath a car, even when it has got a wheel or two missing. Other makers point out that by either removing the spectacles, or folding them up out of the way, the cross-bar can also be chained to the front of a damaged vehicle, thereby usurping an advantage of the old crane and sling outfits. In any case, if the lift is mounted under the vehicle floor, and enough space is left on the deck above, there is no reason why a traditional jib crane should not be fitted as well. It all adds enormously to the versatility of what is already an indispensable piece of machinery, so indispensable that the legal standing of heavy or light under-reaches — does the boom projection count as vehicle overhang, in which case is it excessive? — will have to be resolved in their favour.

There are other convenience factors to spectacle lifts. Not many multi-storey or underground car parks have got enough headroom to allow crane-style lifting of breakdowns, while the few vertical inches taken up by a spectacle-lift device can always be found. And since neither their cost nor weight is excessive it is practicable to fit them to roadside repair rescue vans — if the breakdown can be put right, all well and good; if not, then it is towed away quickly without potentially dangerous delay.

Since the tail boom section of a lift is stowed vertically for travelling it can also be pressed into service as a crane jib, or fairlead, in partnership with an electrically-powered deck-mounted winch. This combination is handy for not-too-complicated off-road recovery jobs, but because all too often the recovery vehicle chassis is rather light for its role in life, operators with damage-free units do well to bear in mind the prospect of overloaded rear axles and underloaded front axles. The quantities of ballast that have to be built in around the front bumpers of many light recovery vehicles is a constant reminder of the risks they run, and so for that matter are the jockey wheels that some makers supply for fitting under the lift boom. These additional wheels are intended to relieve the vehicle rear axle of some weight, and although there is something rather makeshift about the idea, it does mean that units can be built on chassis with the shortest of wheelbases, a very useful feature in congested streets and car parks.

Generally the versatility and robustness needed for off-road recovery of cars and similar-sized vehicles is better provided by units which are essentially small hydraulic cranes working in combination with power-ful winches, and mounted on chassis of up to the 7.5 tonnes mark. In Britain too hydraulic simplicity is supplanting the elaboration of small twin-boom wreckers in light recovery. When genuine dual-purpose small wreckers are really needed the Americans have developed a scheme that seems to meet most requirements — a light space-frame, twin-boom or hydraulic crane unit under the tail of which is a damage-free spectacle frame that can be raised and lowered by the recovery unit winch and cables. Out of use, the frame flips forward to lay on the vehicle deck, well clear of the slings and A-frames used in conventional towing.

With the Holmes version of this dual purpose arrangement, the wheel frame is arranged so that it can slew sideways until it is substantially parallel to and in line with its wrecker, and in this position it can be inveigled under the wheels of a car parked in a line of other vehicles, thereby allowing the car to be trolleyed out.

Of course in a suspended tow one pair of wheels will still be revolving. When they are not those on the driving axle all should be well, provided that if it is the front wheels which are on the ground the steering is firmly locked and secured in the straight-ahead position. And provided also that wheels which are not rotating in their normal direction are checked quite frequently for tightness, for the securing nuts readily work loose on long fast tows in reverse. When the driving wheels are on the ground another complication may well creep in, for as they rotate they will be driving the gearbox from the back instead of the front, and lubrication problems are likely to develop. Indeed, most car makers place limits on the distance a car may be towed, and the towing speed, particularly when it has an automatic transmission.

For such light vehicles a serviceable solution to this problem is the towing dolly, a light, usually four-wheeled frame that can be secured under a jacked-up car, and whose running gear can be used safely for any sensible speed and distance. Although the basic idea in towing dollies is simple enough some ingenuity has gone into finding quicker and more convenient ways of installing them under casualties. Most designs now are variants on a straightforward theme — cross-bars longer than the car width are placed on each side of a pair of wheels, and on each pair of ends a two-wheeled trolley is attached. Then a simple jacking movement with a long handle raises the cross-bars and car wheels, and the assembly is made secure for travelling. Dollies which incorporate automatic self-steering devices that are said to help prevent a towed vehicle from snaking are made, and the German Sedelmeyer company produces a four-wheeled bogie for placing under just one wheel — despite a somewhat odd appearance the resulting seven-wheeled car runs and steers quite smoothly.

A broken down lorry is just a broken down lorry — its driver will probably be inclined to kick it and walk away. But a car that fails may be much loved by a whole family, and wise recovery men do well to remember the point when they arrive to bring it, and quite possibly a tearful wife and children, to safety and succour. Most inappropriate in such circumstances would be the traditional elderly Land Rover, complete with coil of greasy rope serving as passenger seats.

That was the thinking of the commercially-owned recovery clubs, the Automobile Association and the Royal Automobile Club, when they began their transporter breakdown services — each car was likely to contain several passengers, all of whom would expect to be carried onward in a clean comfortable vehicle. One approach was to use suitably fitted out vans, or better still Range Rovers, hauling close-coupled drawbar trailers that were hardly more than a pair of channels to take the casualty's wheels, and a hand-operated winch to load it. Such trailer combinations answer well enough, but great care in achieving a proper balance is necessary when loading and securing down, and the driver must pay continuous attention to what his vehicle, its trailer, and the load are doing — the combination can easily become unstable at speed or in bad road conditions.

Some nasty accidents have tended to turn sentiment away from simple trailers, and the several makers of more elaborate and refined units are at pains to explain that their properly-engineered designs, carried on four or six wheels, with tilting decks and electric winches, are a far cry from the earlier primitives. In any case, these larger trailers can only be towed by heavier vehicles, a factor which in itself adds to stability.

However trailer combinations do have the operating advantage that when there are no breakdowns to recover the towing vehicle can be earning its keep doing something else, but as the idea of back-to-base car recovery grew, the obvious step forward was to adopt light lorries as special purpose transporters for the work — such vehicles had been used for years in transporting builders plant and other machinery. Plenty of small-wheeled chassis are available, and in the longest wheelbase forms there is enough chassis space to allow for equipping them with roomy crew cabs, fitted out with carpeting, luggage space, reclining seats, and other comforts designed to appeal to passengers, and assuage the disappointment of a spoiled day out or holiday. Meanwhile the failed car can be securely mounted behind the cab, and then the whole outfit may go as fast and as far as the law allows, with no worries about stability.

The simplest form of transporter body is of course just a flat platform, inclined at the back to form a beaver tail, and with a pair of detachable channel section ramps. With a winch, hand powered or electric, one man can haul anything with wheels up and on to the deck. But as front and rear overhangs on cars have increased, and such items as airdams, exhaust systems, and number plates get more fragile and ever nearer to the ground, so it becomes more difficult to avoid scraping these expensive details when the angle of loading exceeds 10°, which is a quite moderate slope. A ready solution is to tip the platform with an hydraulic ram, which removes the need for a beaver tail hump and also flattens the angle of the detachable or slide-out ramps that are still needed. But best of all is a slideback transporter, in which the loading deck is winched backward along its chassis until it reaches overbalancing point, when it slopes down to the ground to form the easiest vehicle of all to load. It shows to great advantage when a badly damaged car is being loaded — a car that would not be able to track properly up a pair of narrow ramps. It is also, of course, the most expensive, and while the cost can be justified when a transporter is loaded and unloaded several times a day, less intensive users seem to manage perfectly well with cheaper equipment — just as they manage without the hydraulically-operated ramps which some de-luxe designs provide.

A curiosity in user preference with transporters is in the fairly basic matter of the deck. Some prefer a level and essentially smooth (probably chequerplated) surface from end to end and side to side; others buy bodywork which is not much more than a pair of channels for casualty wheels — often with a wide gap between the channels. Another design appears to be an attempt to combine flat and channeled decks, using a pressed sheet metal floor panel which incorporates a shallow well between the runways. Channel enthusiasts reckon the weight they save can make a difference in the legal carrying capacity equal to that between the weights of a Jaguar and a Rolls-Royce — flat deck owners aver that their machines can also load and carry three-wheelers and badly distorted wrecks. Perhaps the real reason is that increasing specialization in the industry is leading some firms to undertake transport only, not recovery, and so they prefer to use specialized equipment.

It is in response to the perceived need by operators for maximum versatility in their equipment that the French Fiault concern fits a crane jib between the legs of a partially split deck, while the Italian Isoli company produces a tilt deck transporter with hydraulic winch and spectacle frame lift — and a full-scale telescopic recovery crane boom, this latter arranged to lie out of use at chassis level between the twin runways of the tilt platform. Isoli, catering primarily for the Italian market, also produces for recovery use what are essentially lorry-mounted slewing hydraulic cranes with capacities of 12 tonnes at about 12 ft radius, pointing out that such machines give their owners the capability to take on ordinary lifting work when business is slack.

Unfortunately it takes an appreciable length of time to load any transporter, simple or elaborate, and the operation of setting up ramps, or slide-tilting the body, and getting the intended load lined up and winched up must all be done in the middle of the carriageway. City police authorities quite reasonably take a poor view of the chaos this can cause in streets already choked to a near-standstill, while no-one who has seen the accident statistics wants to be stationary on a motorway for any longer than is absolutely necessary. In the circumstances spectacle lifts are finding a new niche as local pick up and run scouting units, liaising with transporters at convenient lay-bys and suburban side streets.

So far the huge majority of transporters have been based on conventional front engine, rear wheel drive, light truck chassis, but intriguing possibilities have opened up with the advent of volume-produced front-wheel drive commercials with carrying capacities of up to 2 tons. Ty-Rite has seized on the idea and is producing a super low level transporter based on a Peugeot-Talbot converted to a six-wheeler, with its load deck positioned down between the four single rear wheels. Ramp loading angles with this are very small, and the concept clearly has great potential.

Even a simple transporter can have its refinements. A winch is essential, and if miniature bollards are strategically placed along each side of the deck, it will be possible to use them in conjunction with the winch rope to help guide on board even the most grievously distorted victim of a crash. Oily surfaces make some sort of friction surfacing on the deck highly desirable, but it mustn't be too effective or locked wheels can't be skidded over it.

Very sturdy tying down points — with, ideally, a strong rail firmly mounted along both sides — are a necessity, and so is some means of securing undamaged cars without marking them. In this connection modern nylon strapping, tightening winches and fittings — all of them virtually identical to the sort of equipment used by sensible hauliers to secure general cargo — are a vast improvement over the time-honoured bits of hemp rope and rusty chain. Another cause for steady complaint among recoverymen is the absence of worthwhile towing or securing eyes on modern cars, even though some governments insist on eyes being provided. (But car-buyers are not easily persuaded to pay a higher price to include such things any more than they are by efforts to sell them safety.) As a refinement, or in deference to the feelings of sensitive clients, canvas curtains are sometimes fitted around a transporter to conceal its contents although, in fact, curtained transporters are more likely to be employed in carrying cars that have been specially prepared for exhibitions or film work.

Quite recently is has dawned on some owners that a very useful accessory indeed can be the kind of self-loading crane commonly fitted behind the cabs of lorries. General purpose designs from Atlas, HAP, Hiab and others have maximum capacities around the 3-6 ton-metre mark, and the larger ones are quite capable of, for instance, lifting a car from a roadside ditch straight on to the transporter. This is useful, but Ty-Rite has taken the idea much further with rather more powerful units. One of these can lift a full-sized car which is parked behind the transporter, power in its telescopic boom, and put the car on to its own deck. Another reaches out to lift a car that is third in line sideways.

The perfect answer, this, for frustrated drivers who are boxed in all round, and an interesting alternative to the units developed for use by police forces in removing cars parked in line. These machines, reminiscent of the launching gear used for ship's lifeboats, have a pair of davits which are lowered to pick up a car and swing it on to the deck of an otherwise conventional heavy platform lorry. But the police, in moving parked cars without the permission of owners, are in a delicate position with regard to causing any damage, and so equipment used by them or on their behalf (city forces are likely to be making increasing use of private companies to remove illegally parked vehicles) has to be rather special.

Cars are not heavy but they are long, and a transporter able to take one behind another is getting pretty unwieldy, although a few such have been built. Some single-car units are fitted with spectacle lifts for suspend-towing second vehicles but this is not altogether satisfactory for long journeys, although the hydraulically-operated lifting frame does make a useful full-width stabilizer for use while a casualty is being winched aboard.

Yet there is money to be earned in long-distance recovery at home and abroad, particularly since the growth in foreign touring holidays. In Britain, where restrictions on vehicle height are generous, and providing their owners can find enough work to keep them busy, double-decked truck and trailer transporters of the kind used for delivering new cars can also be used for making multi-vehicle collections and deliveries of breakdowns. But for more typical operators, and for maximum flexibility in international work the French Jige, and Ty-Rite in association with its Danish Falck partners, have made double-decked transporters on four-wheeled chassis. These can manage two or three cars comfortably, with the upper deck folding down for self-loading, and they are also capable of hauling a third or fourth car if required on a spectacle lift.

Above *An extreme case — but usually it costs more than the vehicles are worth to straighten out the damage caused to cars in crashes. Quite badly damaged heavy commercials on the other hand can often be rebuilt, a factor that influences recovery techniques.*

Below *Volume produced chassis, including many Fords, are favoured as the bases for recovery trucks bought for intensive use. First price is low, servicing quick and cheap, and the special equipment they carry can be readily transferred to other chassis of similar type.*

Above *Traditional tool of the recovery industry, a Land-Rover with crane jib and slings. Many of those still in use are hand-winched, but this Harvey Frost is electrically powered. Modern car design has turned sentiment away from such attractive simplicity.*

Below *In a bid to restore Land-Rover fortunes in recovery, Brimec is using a long wheelbase version as base for its Towlift spectacle frame unit. In place of the usual pick-up back, the Brimec has a specially-constructed deck with an electric winch fitted at the front.*

Above *Such is the versatility of twin-booms that even a small one can recover more than cars. Adding a spectacle lift boom and frame to this Ford Cargo-mounted example increases its repertoire still further. Its size gives it the stamina to lift-tow light commercials too.*

Right *In an interesting attempt to get some benefits of twin-booms without the high first cost, the operator produced this Transit-mounted fixed lifting frame. The wide-spread boom heads, with separate winches, gave flexibility in hauling with secure lift and tow.*

Above *An appealing oddity of the 1950s. The chassis is an early Leyland Cub, perhaps 1931 or 1932 vintage, on to which a proud owner has grafted an American coupé body. The lifting gear also appears to be home-made — why it was fitted with a roof is not clear.*

Below *Not many light recovery vehicles are based on Bedford chassis, but this CF was taken by a dealership for its new Holmes Cadet hydraulic unit. Dolly wheels are commonly supplied but less often used — operators prefer to use a spectacle lift or transporter.*

Above *Twin winches are useful in righting light vehicles that roll after an accident. One rope can be arranged to take the vehicle weight as it descends; the other provides a turning effort. Keeping both ropes taut allows a casualty to be lowered gently.*

Above right *The Sedelmeyer TowLift recovery unit is unusual in that the telescopic crane superstructure can be rotated through a full circle. This feature makes it possible to lift cars out of parked lines without having to block the street while manoeuvring into position.*

Right *Holmes, conscious of the general move to underlifts, adds one to its standard Commander single boom unit, using the same hydraulic system. When it is out of use, the frame folds forward in order not to obstruct conventional winched recovery operations.*

Above *In the absence of anything quite like them on the British market, large American pick-ups have a certain vogue among operators. The traditional virtues of the Jeep suit it well for the purpose, adding a simple jib and powerful winch making it a useful tool.*

Below *The General Motors pick-ups are liked for their eyecatching appearance. This Chevrolet Silverado carries what amounts to an elaborate form of the single fixed boom — it was made by Vulcan, and does not extend. Luffing is by hand only, and a single winch is fitted.*

Above *A casualty that is past caring about further body distortion. Increasingly the design of modern cars makes it unwise to raise them from the extremities, and the only safe way to lift them is from the wheels — or at points very close to the wheels.*

Below *The Vulcan Cradle Snatcher, here mounted on a Bedford chassis, and demonstrating how with the aid of a spreader bar and straps it can lift light commercial vehicles from their wheels. Distance pieces prevent the vertical straps from damaging casualty panel work.*

An early TFL version of the spectacle frame under-lift, capable of being fitted without much modification to suitable light commercials, and with its own self-contained hydraulics. A telescopic cross-beam permitted adjustment to match the track width of any car.

While its traditional range of recovery cranes and equipment were ideal for crash recovery, the rapidly growing demand for damage-free wheel-lifts spurred Harvey Frost into designing and making one of its own. The Ford A-series chassis gave good capacity.

With a little ingenuity spectacle frames can also be used in place of more conventional recovery equipent. Damaged vehicles can be raised from an end by chaining back to the axle. An advantage is the frame is still free to pivot, giving good manoeuvrability.

Fitting a winch just behind the cab, and adding a fairlead to the spectacle frame cross-bar, allows a wheel-lift machine to undertake more complicated recovery jobs than would otherwise be the case. With a snatch block or two the unit becomes quite versatile.

Faced with a daunting total of thirty odd breakdowns and accidents a day, the Hong Kong harbour tunnel authority has equipped itself with a pair of Toyota Landcruisers. Each has a Ty-Rite spectacle frame and an impressive steel joist nudge bar.

Dollies provide a convenient way of supporting one end of a vehicle for recovery. Several kinds are available — most can be assembled under the vehicle, with means of lifting incorporated in them. One elaboration provides Ackermann steering to ensure good tracking.

Above *A suitable dolly, used in conjunction with a spectacle lift, makes it possible to carry out recoveries with all wheels off the ground. In the absence of a proper transporter this will guard against risk of transmission or other damage caused by towing a 'dead' car.*

Below *Although skates are no longer in fashion for heavy or light recovery, units of this kind have obvious uses. Their compact size and considerable articulation mean they can be used in restricted areas next to walls or kerbs, and allow a vehicle to be moved.*

Above *Close-coupled drawbar trailers do not have a good reputation for stability, and an added problem in using them for vehicle recovery is the paramount need for loads to be accurately placed and balanced in relation to the towing vehicle.*

Below *When this drawbar horse box flipped on to its side it completely inverted the towing vehicle. Fortunately the two horses were not badly damaged, but extracting them became a difficult job — one that taxed the recovery operators and their equipment.*

Left *Purpose-built recovery trailers like the Hazlewood are satisfactorily used in their hundreds, behind towing vehicles of suitable capacity. Loading ramps and powered winches make the trailers quick and easy to load, and a flat deck gives versatility.*

Below left *Legal stipulations governing vehicle gross weights make it essential for some operators to pare their equipment to an irreducible minimum. For such users Harvey Frost produces a light-weight trailer with simple wheel channels — and scarcely a superfluous ounce.*

Below *The end of a not-so-perfect holiday. Changes in the patterns of breakdowns and in the kinds of people involved meant that a new kind of recovery transporter had to be evolved, capable of swiftly collecting vehicles, and of accommodating their passengers.*

Right *The Marquiss cab extentions used on the Ford Cargo chassis which it adapts for its transporters are a good example of the standards of comfort provided for passengers who have been involved in breakdowns. Often long journeys will be made, and comfort is essential.*

Below right *Somewhat unusually in a transporter of this calibre only a single cab was fitted — but Marquiss supplied it to a car dismantler who wanted something better suited to long fast journeys than the roughly adapted secondhand lorries common to the scrap vehicle fraternity.*

Below *The long gentle slope that is produced by the Brimec slideback transporter body makes winching necessary only in the case of casualties. The sub-frame is tipped, and the deck rolled back, by hydraulic rams; loading can therefore be a 'clean hands' job for one operator.*

Above *Keeping unladen weight to an absolute minimum is important for some users with some transporters, hence the use of channels instead of a deck for casualty wheels. The slide-out loading ramps are lighter and easier than fully detachable ones for the operator to use.*

Above left *The search for versatility had led Isoli — and others — to add a hydraulic crane to an otherwise conventional transporter. Out of use, the jib lies between the wheel channels. Stabilizers to lift the rear wheels off the ground are essential during craning.*

Left *Nylon webbing of the safety strap kind is ideal for securing casualties on to transporters. Hand ratchet devices are used to pull the straps up tight. This transporter body also has sturdy rave rails, useful things for roping down loads of all kinds.*

Above *TIR-style tilts to conceal cargoes from prying eyes. Highly-prepared cars for exhibition or for use in film work are usually transported in protective obscurity. The tipping six-wheeled trailer is unusual among drawbar units. It is hydraulically operated.*

Below *Water has a great attraction for cars that are inclined to roll away, and wise drivers park parallel to rivers rather than at right-angles to them. A houseboat prevented this runaway from reaching deep water, and it was recovered by straightforward winching.*

Above *It rolled in undamaged — and was hauled out again, hardly damaged. Another fortunate owner who found the progress of his new car stopped by a boat, and incidentally provided an opportunity to demonstrate the value of high level winching by a twin-boom recovery unit.*

Below *Standard behind-the-cab lorry loading cranes are finding a place for themselves in recovery work. Their outreach is enough to lift cars from roadside ditches and similar locations, and they can easily load transporters with vehicles no longer capable of rolling.*

Above *Given a suitable spreader frame, and a car which has an underbody not likely to be damaged (or damaged further) by the process, the larger loading cranes are capable of lifting a vehicle out of a parking lot and placing it on their own deck.*

Below *An elaborate means of lifting individual cars from a line of parked vehicles was built by Telehoist for police use — 'damage-free' operation was deemed essential. Spreader beams are adjustable in both directions, stabilizers are fitted, and operation is hydraulic.*

Above *The Leyland Landmaster is an unusual chassis to find in recovery work — this one has a tilt-bed body, with the added facility of a spectacle lift. This combination has proved to be particularly useful for moving fleet and rental vehicles between depots.*

Below *Other approaches to the problem of low cost bulk vehicle movements are the double-decked transporters made by Brimec and others, using rigid four-wheeled chassis as a base. Adding a spectacle lift is an economical way of increasing capacity when it is needed.*

Chapter 4

Some theory and some law

In the Construction and Use Regulations — a huge work which is so complete and precise in its requirements that seemingly it leaves almost nothing for vehicle designers to do — the categories of vehicles, those likely to be used in recovery work, have a whiff of Edwardian stiff-collared elegance about them. There are locomotives and motor tractors, heavy motor cars and motor cars and, since none of them were specifically intended to include wreckers, the conditions attached to their use have more than an echo of other times about them too.

Locomotives are defined as weighing more than 7,370 kg and to be fitted only for towing. They may haul up to three trailers — which because of carefully stipulated and tight limits on both overall train length and the lengths of individual trailers sounds more attractive than it really is. In fact while some recovery units are certainly to be classed as locomotives they do not fit comfortably into this class, and often appear to be at variance with the regulations. Among other things, maximum speeds running light or while towing are lower than those for other kinds of commercial vehicles, and in some circumstances a mate or assistant must accompany a driver. An odd concession allows locomotives to be marginally wider than the 2.5 m common to other kinds of vehicles.

When the unit weight is below 7,370 kg then the vehicle officially becomes a motor tractor and may tow one laden trailer, two if they are both empty, and a mate is required unless the tow is suspended. The commonest forms of motor cars, heavy or light, used in recovery are the ordinary kinds of transporters.

In making a claim for any exemption from conditions which govern the use of most other kinds of vehicle, the main argument to be put forward by the owner of a unit is that his bona fide recovery vehicle is specially adapted for its purpose with fixed lifting gear, that it carries nothing other than the tools and equipment needed to perform its duties as a recovery vehicle, and is used only as such. This seems clear enough (although it appears that the 'fixed lifting gear' could be classed as goods being transported), until transporters are taken into consideration, for while they too carry fixed means of handling a casualty (if only a winch) and are often used to provide immediate assistance for a breakdown — another factor which is taken to qualify a recovery vehicle — they are equally certainly able, and are used, to carry vehicles and loads other than breakdowns. In any case there is a fine line to be drawn between a broken down car and a scrap one. Lawyers in courts have spent hours debating this point, usually deciding that a scrapper going to its last home should be classed as goods. The sensible course adopted now by most commercial transporter users is to licence them fully as goods vehicles, which at least overcomes one cause for dissent.

An inadvertent and unfortunate effect of the general licensing structure for goods vehicles in Britain is that has tended to encourage the use of chassis that are really too light for transporter work. Up to 7.5 tonnes gross weight no Operator's Licence is needed; above that fairly low limit owners become liable to the rigours of haulage law.

Because of their ambivalent status, recovery units not adapted to carry a load need not be subjected to the regular and government controlled examination and testing that virtually all other commercial vehicles have to undergo. This seems illogical, but at least there is the argument that most of them cover quite low mileages. More importantly, there is no requirement for compulsory testing of the lifting and other equipment mounted on the vehicle, although the lifting gear is frequently worked to its maximum capacity and beyond. However most insurers want to see a current test certificate before providing cover, and prudent owners make sure in addition that their ropes, chains and slings are beyond reproach. Some, perhaps, do not.

Attempts are being made to introduce some kind of industry-based competency assessment and certification for operators and it is easy to see the attraction of such a scheme, but it implies that at some time a means will be found to prevent uncertificated operators from being employed on recovery work. Meanwhile in one regard at least the law has stepped in, demanding that before a recoveryman may deal with vehicles containing any of a large number of potentially dangerous substances, he will have sat through a course of instruction in handling hazardous goods and hold a valid certificate to prove it. This is no more than a logical extension of the legal requirement that any driver in charge of hazardous goods must be properly trained in safe handling techniques and suitable emergency procedures. In addition a wrecker driver must hold the appropriate driving licence, probably heavy goods.

Recovery vehicles enjoy few exemptions from the laws which control all kinds of road transport, and those few are nearly all concerned with operating rather than technical matters. In fact the only concessions really worth bothering about in Britain are concerned with rates of vehicle taxation, permitted hours of work for drivers, drivers work records, and things of that sort. Certainly the vehicles and the ways in which they are used on public roads must be kept within the dimensional restrictions laid down in the Regulations and so too must the vehicles they recover. Moreover, there is no relief from the all-embracing requirement that any motor vehicle on a public road is appropriately licensed and insured.

The traditional dilemmas in licensing wreckers proper are not easily resolved, because the taxation of ordinary lorries is based on weight, a factor which is clearly not applicable. Another complication is that some units are handmaidens to bus or lorry fleets and see little use; others are worked hard and very nearly continuously by commercial recovery operators. This factor alone makes it impossible to design an equitable taxation system. Probably the only sensible course is to accept that high mileage machines will supplement what amounts to a nominal registration fee by the taxation revenue derived from the increased quantity of fuel they use.

There are some other interesting provisions in the regulations for recovery. If the casualty is being lift-towed then its brakes need not be usable; if its steering is effective then its brakes must be used — either by someone in the cab, or by the wrecker driver. In reality braking can become a worrysome thing, and wherever possible air lines are run between the two vehicles so that all the brakes can be controlled from the front. Competent operators make every attempt to get brakes working and capable of being applied from the towing vehicle. The general requirement for virtually all vehicles to have pneumatic tyres is waived for breakdowns, thereby making it possible to use heavy duty small wheeled dollies and skates, not that they are often used these days.

Curiously while a tow rope or chain may not be longer than 4.5 m, a drawbar can be to any length. Recovery units are among the few vehicles allowed to use flashing amber beacons — while towing and at an incident, but not on the way to it — and few operators can resist the temptation to take full advantage of the concession. There is much, much, more in the same vein contained in the Regulations, some of it apparently contradictory, and much of it puzzling.

'Give me a good six-wheeled wrecker,' said the vastly experienced recovery man, 'and I'll make it better by cutting off the third axle.' He exaggerated, but there is enough logic in his prejudice to make the idea worth exploring.

From the recovery point of view, axle weights are about the most taxing of the stipulations laid down in the 'C and U Regs'. The 16 tons maximum permitted gross vehicle weight for four-wheelers (unless they are coaches, when a little more is allowed) is divided so that 6 tons may be imposed on the front axle and 10 tons on the rear. A typical recovery unit will weigh perhaps 9 tons when it is ready for work, with about three of those tons on its back axle, and because it was designed for recovery work it has a long wheelbase of, say, 15 ft. It is desirable for at least two-thirds of the overall length to be in front of the rear axle. But of course, even though designers always make great efforts to keep the rear overhang, from the back axle centre to the point at which a lifting force is exerted, as small as possible, it is still a considerable distance. The result is that in a lift and tow job the back axle becomes in effect the fulcrum point of a see-saw. That fulcrum is already carrying its share of the wrecker's own weight on one side, and to that must be added the casualty weight on the other. The total load it can carry legally may not, of course, be more than 10 tons.

Now, a twin-boom or crane will have an overhang of 5 ft at least from its rear axle centre to the point at which its A-frame is coupled to the vehicle about to be raised, and a large casualty, loaded, will have a front axle weight of 6 tons. If such a typical vehicle can be lifted at a point near to its front bumper, then the weight transference which automatically occurs reduces the weight that is to be raised to, probably, no more than $4\frac{1}{2}$ tons. By the time this $4\frac{1}{2}$ tons is transmitted forward through the lifting equipment (which process will probably amplify it a bit) and reaches the wrecker chassis, then the rear axle of this vehicle will still be carrying a total of not more than 10 tons. All well and good, but alas, that part of the casualty weight which is automatically transferred when the front wheels left the ground has to go somewhere, and it ends up on the casualty rear wheels — which thereby become considerably, and illegally, overloaded at about 11-$11\frac{1}{2}$ tons.

That snag can easily be overcome by using an under-reach machine, coupled up so as to lift a breakdown from its front axle; little weight transference can take place then. Not, that is, on the casualty, but the load which this method of lifting will impose on the recovery unit is applied at such a considerable distance behind its rear wheels that the axle is in grave danger of being, in legal terms, overloaded. Fit a 13 ton or 15 ton capacity axle by all means; but the law says that on public roads it may not carry more than 10 tons. Off-road of course is another matter, and a heavy duty axle may well be a very sensible thing to have in order to minimize mechanical damage.

The obvious solution is to use instead six-wheelers, with sturdy two-spring or balance beam rear bogies, but simple answers rarely prove to be so simple in practice, and in a multi-axled vehicle the separate parts of the wheelbase also become factors in the calculations. A big drawback is the stipulation in the Construction and Use Regulations that twinned axles as close together as they must be on wrecker chassis can have a joint capacity that is no more than 19 tons. With a two-spring suspension that see-saw effect moves its fulcrum to the bogie centre trunnion, which effectively increases the rear overhang of the vehicle as a whole by a couple of feet at least.

In a sense, the law of diminishing returns sets in, and a wrecker chassis has to be made much bigger to get a relatively modest, if still worthwhile, increase in lifting capacity. Medium and light recovery units very rarely have more than four wheels, but their own weight limits are lower anyway and just as likely to be exceeded while making a suspended tow.

There is no difficulty at all in building high capacity lifting gear, and indeed owners sometimes boast of having 20, 30, or even 40 tons of lifting capacity. With their stabilizers fully extended and their ground anchors in perhaps they have, but it is not possible to mount these musclebound machines on to roadgoing chassis in such a way as to use them on the road at anything like their maximum ratings. In any case, there is not likely to be much call for them to do so. Often, though, there is confusion between lifting and winching capacities and an ordinary large recovery unit, properly built for the work and securely anchored, with its ropes carefully rigged, is quite capable of exerting a winch pull of up to 40 tons. Wrecker design is, in short, a fine exercise in the art of the possible.

But even users who never have need of the apparent lift capacity of six-wheelers still buy them, and not only because they look good. Those additional wheels also mean additional braking power, something that can be very welcome in controlling a train up hill and down dale. In addition, the extra grip and directional stability that comes with a double drive bogie is a comforting thing when road surfaces are bad. And, at the least, a large heavy machine with four sets of tyres biting the ground is a useful thing to have when the winch hydraulic relief valves are popping.

All these problems which are incurred by trying to lift laden lorries rather beg the obvious question; why not unload them first? There are two main reasons why that is often, indeed usually, impracticable. Not only are a lot of the commodities carried by road quite unsuitable for transhipment in public places — hot liquid chocolate or sulphur might present difficulties for instance, and the police would not welcome 25 tons of sand or coal being tipped on a motorway hard shoulder — but speed of clearance is a major factor. Any unexpected blockage on a road is potentially lethal, so wherever possible it pays to pick up a breakdown, loaded or not, and run. It is another reason that under-lifts large and small are so much in favour, but it has to be admitted that owners are very frequently displeased at being confronted with a hefty towing bill when the cause of a breakdown was trivial and quickly put right.

Because the weight on the front wheels of an ordinary rigid lorry with its front axle underneath the engine does not change much whether laden or empty, these wheels are usually carrying something like their maximum load all the time. Even when the vehicle is empty, therefore, there is a risk that if it is lift-towed from the back, weight transference forward will legally overload the front tyres. To try more than a short distance emergency movement of a loaded truck would be to invite disaster. On most modern four-wheeled coaches and buses, however, weight distribution between the two axles is much more even and an empty coach although still quite heavy can be raised at its rear axle(s), or at suitable floor framing very close behind them, without a great deal of risk.

Provided, that is, an under-reach can be found which has enough capacity at its maximum boom extension — for on many coaches a combination of weight and rear overhang now taxes the ability of even the most powerful under-reaches. Indeed there are a few vehicles which add a third difficulty factor, for they possess underfloor complications in the form of engine and transmission ancillaries that make it impossible to find any suitable lifting point. Even when a comparatively simple front-axle lift is contemplated, passenger vehicle transmissions will, more often than not, add yet another problem in that they will suffer serious damage if they are driven from the wheels instead of the engine.

No gearbox will be improved by such treatment (usually gearboxes rely on being driven conventionally for their lubrication), and vehicle instruction manuals often stipulate that only very short tows may be made without disconnecting the cardan shaft, or withdrawing the axle half-shafts. This serves for nearly all lorries, but drive axles for buses are often not suitable for roadside dismantling. A newer, yet further, difficulty is becoming apparent on vehicles equipped with modern computer-controlled gearboxes which rely on speed sensors driven by the road wheels.

Experienced hands will, incidentally, remember to disconnect propeller shafts (and wind off spring brakes) while a rolled vehicle is still lying on its side. A standing grievance held by recovery operators against vehicle manufacturers is their persistence in using many small bolts, inaccessibly positioned, to secure the flanges of transmission shafts and other items that may have to be taken off in an emergency. Removing these by the roadside in the conditions surrounding any breakdown is a thoroughly nasty job, however it becomes a great deal easier when the running gear is chest-high and spanners can be brought to bear properly! Fortunately weight transference is no great problem with artic tractors, in which rear suspend-tows are much to be preferred over dismantling their transmissions.

Provided a breakdown is being taken to 'a place of safety or repair', the law allows some leniencies in recovery operations, and one of the most useful is in the matter of road train lengths. By the time a passenger vehicle built to the maximum permissable length of 12 m is hitched to an averagely lengthy wrecker (maximum permissable length 11 m not counting its crane, although most are shorter) by means of a conventional tow-bar or A-frame, the overall length of the train will be well outside the normal permissable limit of 18 m for vehicles hauling drawbar trailers. Here the under-reach is a help, for apart from providing a generally handier tractor-trailer combination, it requires only a very small clearance between its tailgate and the casualty front panelling. Probably an unlikely-sounding 6 in wide gap will be enough to allow wrecker and trailer to negotiate minimum radius bends. It sometimes baffles those not conversant with such things to find that motor vehicles are legally regarded as trailers when they are towed, even though there are steersmen steering them. But then courts have decided that even vehicles without engines are considered to be mechanically propelled for as long as they are capable of being rebuilt.

It must be said that most ordinary people encountering a regular road train that is 18 m (59 ft) in length will reckon it quite long enough, but a full-sized articulated lorry will measure 15.5 m from bumper to under-run guard, so when an artic has to be recovered it presents dimensional difficulties. Furthermore, since it legally comprises two separate parts, the regulation which forbids most kinds of vehicles from hauling two trailers can only be interpreted as preventing also a coupled-up artic from being towed. Clearly this produced an impossible situation and so a partial relaxation of the law allows a coupled but unladen artic to be, for recovery purposes, regarded as one vehicle. The concession is not extended to laden vehicles which, legally, must be uncoupled before being moved or else towed only by a locomotive. The double-think extends to heavy recovery ambulances; clearly two-wheeled trailers these, but not counted as such when in use.

Since a large number of articulated lorries — typically fuel tankers operated by oil companies — are not regularly uncoupled in normal service and therefore have no landing gear fitted to their semi-trailers, recovery operators and policemen in charge of traffic incidents can find themselves making difficult decisions. This 'Alice in Wonderland' approach extends to the potentially troublesome matter of overall train length, for although the towed artic — empty, of course — is 'one' vehicle, the train of which it becomes a part may be up to 25.9 m long, the limit for those few combinations which may legally include two trailers. In emergencies old hands recite as a litany: 'We are clearing the Queen's Highway!' — an incantation which is powerful enough to fend off even the most difficult and enquiring specimens of officialdom, for a few hundred yards, at least.

The problems created by manoeuvrability are another reason why double-drive six-wheelers are not more widely used. (Eight-wheelers are almost a curiosity because, in addition, there is a lack of suitable rear suspension, gearbox and engine combinations.) Unless the recovery chassis is quite short it will not be able to tow maximum length casualties. If, on the other hand, it is short enough to perform this work legally, then it may not be long enough to allow for proper weight distribution over its own axles. While even a heavy duty twin-boom need not take up a great deal of deck space, a big under-reach does require a fairly long chassis for both installation and weight distribution.

Without his winches any recovery operator would be lost, and if a good long, strong, pull is a desirable thing to have then it would be reasonable to assume that a longer, stronger, one is better still. In practice there are big practical difficulties for anyone who tries to step outside the usual run of winch sizes; design is largely a matter of proportion, and in the space available on the back of a recovery vehicle those proportions limit the physical dimensions of the winch.

The story begins with the rope diameter, which is determined by the maximum load likely to be hauled, and a convenient rope length. The diameter will always be kept as small as possible in order to get the maximum flexibility (and wire rope is indeed remarkably flexible) but there is a minimum diameter drum around which such a rope can be wound — any smaller and it will be permanently damaged — and if a very long rope is wound on to the drum it will build up a great many layers. But winches exert their most powerful pull when their drums are nearly empty; as the coils of rope are wound on, the strength of the pull steadily diminishes, so there is a practical limit to the number of rope layers, and therefore rope length, that can be used.

If the drum diameter cannot be increased then another apparent way of increasing its capacity is to make the drum longer so that it can take more turns in each layer. Unfortunately in this kind of work that isn't possible either. When a well-designed winch hauls in the load its rope will wind itself neatly on to the drum, forming tidy layers as it goes; if it does not lay properly then the resulting tangle will cause serious damage to the rope strands. But this self-layering depends on the angle of the incoming cable being quite small; compel the rope to travel from end to end of a long drum and this angle of veer will also become bigger. Then the turns of cable will just bunch up in the middle. In the event quite the best way of increasing the winching capacity of a wrecker is to fit a pair of winches instead of just one — two smaller, and therefore longer, ropes and of course an ability to pull together, or in two directions at once.

Winch speeds and drives are other limiting factors, for while it would sometimes be very pleasant to have a cable sailing along, with whatever it is hauling covering the ground at speed, common prudence dictates that in most recovery jobs a slowly travelling rope with the whole operation fully under control and capable of being stopped in an instant, is a far better way of achieving a satisfactory outcome. So it is necessary to use some form of gearing to reduce the high speed produced by whatever drives the winch — usually the vehicle engine. Like any other transmission train this process transforms high speed and low power into low speed and high power — make the speed reduction great enough to turn the winch very slowly and it will exert a tremendous pulling effort while doing so. Again there are practical limits on what can be done, but the use now of hydraulics has at least removed the old difficulties of getting a smooth, steady, drive for the larger units. When, incidentally, a fast travel for the rope is wanted — in running it out from wrecker to casualty, or winding it in when a job is completed — these big winches can be made to freewheel, and they have a crank handle fitted too.

For light vehicle recovery a large variety of electric winches is made, and these neat little units can be bolted down to any convenient part of a recovery truck, and these are also the kind of winch used to self-load transporters, and on the fronts of cross-country vehicles that are likely to get themselves bogged down. Then the winch can be used for self-recovery. Power for these small units comes from the vehicle batteries, so there is a limit to the amount of time they can run, but it is long enough for all practical purposes.

They will all vary to some degree of course, but probably the winches on a big recovery unit will have on them about 200 ft of ⅝ in diameter wire rope. Incidentally, the term wire rope is something of a misnomer since the kinds of rope used in recovery usually have a fibre core around which the wire strands are wound. Such a rope will have a breaking strain of about 15 tons, or a working capacity of 3 tons. But in many operations it is used at least double, and not infrequently quadruple, which explains why the winch may be rated at 40 tons, and also why 200 ft often doesn't leave much to spare. Even when the rope is being used singly, by the time it has been run round an anchor or two in order to change its direction of pull, the available length is soon used up. Light vehicle winches hold perhaps 75 ft of $\frac{3}{8}$ in diameter rope. These small machines shouldn't ever be overstressed (no machine ever should) and if there is a risk, then a bigger one can be called.

The most important point about any winch is its rated safe working load yet this, oddly, is an area of great confusion. American ratings or British ratings? They are not at all the same. Horizontal pull or vertical lift? That can alter the loadings considerably. Different makers and agents — for winches are items of international trade — have different views on such things and present the facts in different ways. Lack of certainty eats in to whatever factors of safety an operator thinks he is relying upon, and too often the declared safety factor is inadequate anyway.

This would be unfortunate even in circumstances where loadings are known with some accuracy, but in the give and take of recovery the best anyone can do is make a guess, informed or otherwise. Certainly the pull required to move a more or less fit vehicle that is standing on its own wheels can vary enormously. On hard standing its resistance may be only 1/25th of its own weight; soft sand or gravel increases the effort needed to a fifth; mud or bog is even worse, half the vehicle weight. Then of course must also be added the resistance caused by any gradient. The ability to call to mind such information when it is required is a mark of the expert, as distinct from the experienced, operator. There is a nice distinction between the two!

Clearly control and organization at any traffic incident, large or small, must be in the hands of one organization, and equally clearly the most obvious body to take charge of events are the police. One of their immediate responsibilities is to call out a suitable recovery operator — one who has adequate equipment and who can be expected to know how to use it.

In less complicated times this would have been the nearest commercial garage, or perhaps even a neighbouring bus company or haulier who was known to have suitable tackle. But times have changed and the informal approach by individual policemen relying on their local knowledge has in many areas given way to a briskly operated procedure which is designed to remove any hint that personal preference, bias even, might take precedence over dispassionate assessment of suitability. In a word, most police forces are wary enough now to operate call-out rosters for recovery firms. Usually the procedure is for the first police team on site to ask drivers who are involved in accidents and breakdowns (if they are fortunate enough to be in a position to be asked) for their preferred recovery agencies — the club system means that this question is not as fatuous as it might appear. If no firm opinion can be obtained then the police control room will be asked to call out an operator. Control then contacts the next suitable firm on a roster — constables out on the road, they emphasize, have no say in deciding who is to be called. Once called, an operator must respond — only a very few failures to do so will soon lead to being struck off the list, and substitutes are frowned upon.

From the operator's point of view the system has two main effects, both of them essentially beneficial. It removes the need for constant jockeying and lobbying for accident work, and in those areas where the police have set themselves the task of regularly vetting operators, it also enforces good standards of equipment, training and performance. In such districts there is a certain cachet about being on 'police lists'; it helps to distinguish between the thoroughly competent and the rest. However the roster system loses some of its edge when lists are almost open-ended or operators are not inspected. It certainly still maintains fairness, but there is no guarantee that the operator called will be big enough or suitably equipped to handle complicated incidents.

However, listing of any kind is not compulsory, and with no less than 55 police authorities in mainland Britain practice varies from place to place, and not only in the manner of calling on recovery teams either. Operators all too frequently find that when they cross a county boundary the enforcement climate changes radically, and what has become accepted practice in one area is much frowned upon in the neighbouring district. Quite possibly local authority by-laws add their own crust to an already indigestible pie.

At least part of the problem here is the impossibility of predicting every combination of events and results that might occur in traffic accidents, thus making it difficult for lawyers to draught, and for police to interpret, consistent recovery law. But there is certainly considerable scope for introducing some improvements and a degree of standardization. And, despite the present regulations offering some scope for rule-bending by the flexibly minded, respectable operators would welcome a more rational approach.

If indeed specialized vehicle recovery can advance from being a new industry to becoming an established one some major changes are likely to occur within its structure. A key factor will be the machines themselves; indications are that most of the makers will have to become more proficient in both design and construction and, as a result, their products will become still more versatile and more costly. This in turn will make them less attractive possessions for the sorts of garages and repair shops who do a bit of recovery work on the side. If this indeed happens then ownership will become concentrated in the hands of dedicated users, who will tend to become larger in size and fewer in number. These concerns would be strong enough to escape from the present subservient role of recovery and be strong enough, if not to dictate terms, at least to become equal partners in negotiations; take part in (and be held to) public contracts; and would be in a position to establish properly assessed and uniform rates for work done.

A remarkable instance of what can be done in this direction is in Denmark, where all the national emergency services, including fire-fighting, are run not by the state but are in the hands of the Falck organization, a commercial operation. A large and comprehensive recovery service is part of this extraordinary enterprise, and the combination of responsibility and size has led it to push the development of specialized vehicles and equipment in a way hardly dreamed of in Britain. In addition Falck recovery staff are properly and formally trained, and their wreckers are well maintained and replaced in good time — such good time, in fact, that secondhand units find a market in Britain.

A blanket private monopoly of this kind is not likely ever to be echoed in Britain, but already there are signs that a few of the very largest providers of vehicle emergency services are considering ways of increasing their influence, and are pressing for a much bigger say in framing regulations and in negotiations with police forces, emergency services and government. If they get their way, then the rest of the industry will be forced into a limited number of mergers or federations in order to survive.

Above *One of the distinguishing marks of a recovery vehicle is that it is permanently fitted with the means of raising and towing a casualty while being incapable of carrying general cargo. It can, however, carry ancillary equipment necessary for its role in life.*

Below *The legal restrictions on operating weights for vehicles were intended to control traffic within general haulage, but inadvertently they also have the effect of persuading operators engaged in light recovery work to buy lightweight chassis.*

Above *Strictly enforced regulations govern the use of vehicles carrying hazardous loads, and these requirements are extended to recovery operators who deal with such vehicles. Drivers are required to undergo specific training, and follow-up refresher courses.*

Above left *Any risk of puncturing or other subsequent damage caused in handling petroleum spirit tankers is reduced when air bags are used for recovery. Even notionally empty tanks can still contain highly inflammable vapour which needs only a spark to ignite.*

Left *Mainstay of many if not most bus fleets was traditionally a time-expired vehicle, cut down and suitably equipped for its new career. The Preston Corporation Leyland Titan is typical of the breed, but underfloor and rear-engined chassis do not adapt so easily.*

Above *Inevitably the army-surplus AEC Matador found its way in to bus fleets but rarely has much work taxed these powerful machines, and usually their lives were spent in semi-retirement. Indeed Matadors are still to be found dozing at the backs of sheds.*

Below *Bus operators increasingly rely on recovery vehicles that are built for the work, on conventional chassis. Where the construction of casualties permits it, the adaptable twin-boom is favoured, but more and more passenger vehicles need under-reach units.*

Left Buses must be capable of leaning at considerable angles — 28° for double deckers, 35° for single deckers — before they roll over, so provided they are standing more or less upright and on fairly firm ground their recovery does not usually present major problems.

Below left Dolly, or 'ambulance', recoveries for heavy vehicles are now quite rare — these two-wheeled trailers must inevitably have small diameter wheels that are shod with solid rubber, and the combination is not ideal for use in modern road traffic conditions.

Below A skate has even more limited application, but there are occasions when a vehicle must be moved for short distances over a smooth hard surface, and there is no more convenient way of carrying one end of an axle. This skate can also be placed under a wheel.

Above *Not quite a reversion to dolly recovery. Instead, the addition of a castor wheel to a spectacle lift can prevent overloading on the rear axle of a recovery vehicle that would otherwise lack sufficient capacity, effectively increasing its payload.*

Above right *A world in which there are no artificial limits on the weights of recovery vehicles, and operating conditions are always difficult and often dangerous. A battle tank forms an ideal base for winching, particularly when a dozing blade is added to its front.*

Right *The British Army Centurion recovery unit weighs nearly 50 tons and it has a road speed of about 20 mph. Rather more significantly it has a maximum winch pull of 105 tons, and anchors big enough to ensure that none of that effort goes to waste.*

Above *Heavyweight champion in civilian recovery for many years was the Diamond T six by four. By general consent, they could move almost anything. But age tells — now they are too slow for long distance towing, although some are still treasured for their winching capacity.*

Below *A distinctly unusual candidate for conversion to civilian use was this elderly ex-Swiss army Magirus Deutz gun tractor. Now it has a large capacity under-reach recovery unit mounted on it, for use by the engineering department of Yorkshire Traction.*

Above *Vehicle recovery operators are rarely surprised by the calls that come for their services, but this became one of the more unusual jobs. The ship was holed and beached, and recovery units were called in to move and place anchors and stabilizing equipment.*

Right *Large animals falling into inaccessable places are a not uncommon cause of calls for the services of recovery operators in rural areas. Once the slings and ropes are placed a horse in a ditch, or a cow in a slurry tank, presents no great difficulties.*

Above *Provided the vehicle on tow is a genuine breakdown being taken to a place of safety or repair there is no legal limit to the overall length of towing unit and casualty. But practical considerations keep long trains off winding side roads.*

Below *The under-reach forms a rapid and convenient way of picking up roadside breakdowns, with the minimum of delay. Because the articulation point is so far behind the towing vehicle a casualty tracks better, with reduced cut-in on corners.*

Bottom *A combination not favoured in British operating conditions but used by the Falck organization in Denmark is a heavy duty transporter that is also fitted with an under-reach for commercial vehicles. An extra refinement is a lorry-loading crane.*

Above *Operators generally want businesslike-looking vehicles, and pay increasing attention to bodywork on recovery units. An added bonus is the creation of space for spacious side lockers; properly used, these make it more difficult to mislay or lose valuable bits of kit.*

Below *Conditions when a big recovery unit is needed. A combined pull is being made — upward to prevent the casualty wheels from digging in and below to move it forward. The unit is a TFL, with sawtoothed racks and crossbar to relieve the boom lifting rams during winching.*

Above *The Scammell-TFL, waiting for a call. While two-axled machines cope perfectly well with most heavy recovery jobs, a double-drive six-wheeler can often be welcome in rough work. Unusually the single boom on this early TFL is a parallel box beam.*

Below *No axle overloading problems are created whichever end of an articulated tractor is raised from the ground, and a convenient way of making such a recovery is with one of the lifting devices which can be quickly attached to a standard fifth-wheel plate.*

Above *A fine demonstration of what is meant by excessive trailer cut-in. A pull from the recovery unit winch on to the top of the concrete beam relieves the nearside bogie wheels from much of the weight they are carrying, making it easier to free them.*

Below *Confusingly, a broken down articulated lorry is legally considered to be one vehicle when it is unladen — at other times, two vehicles. No consideration is given to those artics which are not meant to be uncoupled by the roadside, whether empty or laden.*

Above *To make full use of its lifting capacity a maximum capacity recovery unit like this export Foden with Wreckers International Recoverer equipment must have a wheelbase long enough to provide counterbalance in front for whatever weight is suspended from the back.*

Below *Eight-wheeled chassis are not common in recovery work, for in the opinion of many users they have few virtues not already possessed by six-wheelers. Instead their length is seen as a disadvantage, making them unhandy in general purpose operations.*

Above *American conditions favour long distance towing, high mileages, and therefore premium quality recovery units. This Kenworth is such a machine, fitted with a capacious sleeper cab, under-reach equipment, and demonstrating the virtues of long wheelbase six-wheelers.*

Below *Winches are the heart of any recovery unit that is not used solely for towing, and on heavy vehicles two are better than one. In this Wreckers International installation the winches are hydralically powered — to the right can be seen a band safety-brake.*

Above *From the winches the wire ropes pass over the boom of this Interstater under-reach, and through a pair of swivelling fairleads incorporated in the boomhead. These are self-aligning, allowing the ropes to take up the best line they can and with the least resistance.*

Left *Light auxilliary winches are widely used, particularly in such applications as loading transporters, and on light recovery vehicles — but they are also fitted to rough ground units that may need to self-recover. Any convenient tree will provide a suitable anchor.*

Left *Self-recovery in the long-ago. Provided the two anchormen could keep clear of flying mud, the improvized winch with rope round hub-mounted drum probably worked — but doubt is created by the jacks and timbering that form the cargo for this mudbound Saurer of 1914.*

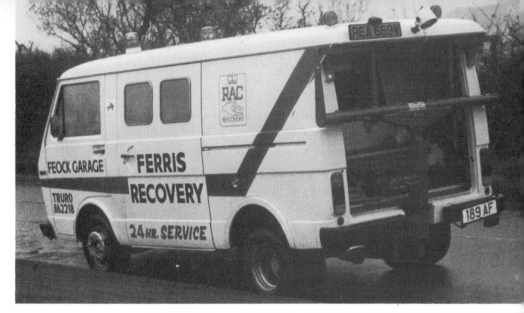

Above *Breakdown-cum-recovery vans form a logical combination of functions that is being adopted by some light recovery operators. If a vehicle can be repaired by the roadside, all well and good, if not it can be towed away with the minimum of delay.*

Right *Changing conditions are encouraging operators to adopt new kinds of equipment to increase speed and safety in recovery. Mobile flood lighting on extending towers is common in the construction industry, and now similar units are being fitted to recovery vehicles.*

Above *To the Automobile Association is due the credit of having popularized the word 'relay' as the generic term for transporter recovery of breakdowns. In common with other operators the AA is moving away from trailers and lightweight chassis.*

Below *Sheer mass is necessary for heavy haulage, and a machine such as this mighty Scammell Constructor would have had no difficulty in towing anything put behind it. But weight is a disadvantage in off-road operations, where haulage capacity is a matter of winching.*

Index

128

Wreck and Recovery

Scammell, 17, *22, 61, 118,*
  120, 126
Sedelmeyer, 76, *85*
Steam wagon, *30*
Steiner, *46*

Telehoist, *97*
TFL, 46, 71, *88, 119, 120*
Thornycroft, *37*
Towing dolly, 76, *89, 90,*
  114
Toyota, *89*
Type approval, 18
Ty-Rite, 48, 79, 80, *89*

Volvo, *119*
Vulcan, 74, *86, 87*

Ward LaFrance, 17

Winches, 41, 42, 75, *85,*
  106, *123, 124*
Wire rope, 108
Wreckers:
  American, 73
  battle tanks, *115*
  cranes, 78, 80, *96, 97,*
    111, 119, 122, 126
  dimensions, 102
  dual purpose, 48, *65*, 75,
    94, 125
  fifth-wheel attachments,
    45, *62, 120*
  fork truck, *64*
  four-wheeled, 101
  hydraulic, 43, *58, 59, 66,*
    73, *84*
  side loaders, *97*
  six-wheeled, 101

special, *38*
spectacle lift, *31, 39*, 72,
  74, *88, 89, 115*, 125
trailers, 77, *92, 95*
transporters, 14, 18, *33,*
  34, 70, 77, *92, 93, 94,*
  97, 98, 111, 126
transporters, double-
  decked, 80, *98*
twin boom, 13, *23, 32,*
  41, *54, 55, 70*, 72, *83,*
  116
under-reach, *30, 31*, 46,
  63, 64, 116, 118, 119,
  122, 123
Wreckers International, 43,
  46, 48, 56, 58, 63, 73,
  122